NO PLACE TO HIDE

NO PLACE TO HIDE

by

Alan LeMond and Ron Fry

A New Earth Book

ST. MARTIN'S PRESS   NEW YORK

CONTENTS

This book is dedicated to Jay Acton, Bob Abel, Representative Edward Koch, Edward R. Boyko, and all the many others who helped us with it. It is also dedicated to Mary Anne, Lisa, Nicole, Daisaku Ikeda, Mr. Sudo, and all the many others for whom the book was written.

Preface:

Who is being watched, and why, and with what

There was, of course, no way of knowing whether you were being watched at any given moment. How often, or on what system, the Thought Police plugged in on any individual wire, was guesswork. It was even conceivable that they watched everybody all the time. But at any rate they could plug in your wire whenever they wanted to. You had to live—did live, from habit that became instinct—in the assumption that every sound you made was overheard, and, except in darkness, every movement scrutinized.

—1984

Perhaps the "scare" quote from George Orwell's classic *1984* has been overdone, but high school students can no longer read the passage and shake their heads in wide-eyed admiration of the man's unabashedly creative imagination. The vision of 1984 crystallized into reality long before that fateful year. Every sound you utter, anywhere, *could* be overheard right now. And every movement *even in darkness* could be scrutinized as easily as watching goldfish in a bowl.

More people today are being bugged, tapped, tailed, probed, watched, and investigated, without their consent, than most of us would ever have thought possible. And the nightmarish, tyrannical world of Orwell creeps upon us at its petty pace from day to day. How often, and on what system, the "Thought Police" are plugged into any individual wire *is* guesswork. And we *should* live under the assumption that every sound we make is being overheard—not only overheard, but recorded and filed. The nation's data banks, both governmental and private, are being systematically and ceaselessly filled with information about us. You would probably be amazed at what they already know about you.

Who are "they"?

Well, "they" are almost every business or government agency with whom you have done business or have been in contact in any way. They are also some of the businesses and agencies with whom you didn't even know you'd had contact. They are the Internal Revenue Service; the Army, Navy, or Air Force Intelligence Division; the Federal Bureau of Investigation; the Justice Department's Civil Disturbance Group; the Department of Housing and Urban Development; your state or local police; the credit bureaus; your bank; and many, many more.

They are all compiling information and filing that information—sometimes indiscriminately—into large computers, where it sits and waits.

The one thing in your favor—so far—is that the data banks are not connected with each other. Each storage bin is still somewhat self-contained. But not for long. They are already working on plans to connect the computers. So that the files of the FHA will be instantaneously available to, say, the FBI. And the files of the banks will be just as speedily available to the IRS, and so on.

Our telephones are being tapped by increasing numbers of government agents, business spies, friends, spouses, and other assorted privacy-invaders, without most of us ever knowing it. We only think we have private lines, for in reality many thousands of telephones all over the country are more or less "party lines" with the subscriber the only one not aware of the party going on.

The telephone has always been a popular location for a listening transmitter, or a "bug," maybe because everybody has one. And maybe because we tend to say things over a telephone we wouldn't dare say anywhere else, except in the strictest privacy. How naive we are.

Because even when we know it's happening, when we read about it almost daily in the newspapers, we go blithely on, either not realizing or not allowing ourselves to realize the effect that the thousands of electronic devices are having on our privacy. Devices—transistorized and miniaturized—that are used to both improve the storage capacity of the computer data banks, and to improve the methods of getting that information in the first place. Information about you and me and all the other private citizens.

If you think that's frightening, look at what the future has in store for us, the bugger's delight: the video telephone. Already one experienced wiretapper has stated publicly that he has doped out a way that will enable him to see right into a subscriber's home.

"But not me," you say, "Nobody's going to spy on me; I've got nothing to hide."

You may not realize how right you are. You have nothing to hide any more because one of those previously mentioned gov ernment agencies became especially interested in your activities at one time . . . or your spouse did, or your boss did for some reason, and they already know all about you.

The reason doesn't have to be earth shattering. You may have cheated on your wife—just a little, or on your income tax. Or you may have bought that new car from a less-than-reputable dealer that the government has its eyes on.

If you're young, maybe you were one of the thousands who joined peace rallies or simply watched, only to be arrested for disorderly conduct. If you're arrested once—even if the case is eventually dismissed—you are on file. You've got a record. You could be brought in again, just as a suspect, merely because of that one inconsequential, and unproven, charge.

As everyone knows, doing something illegal doesn't hurt. Getting caught does. And today, thanks to the ever-thundering march of science and technology, everybody gets caught, somewhere, sometime, for something. Someone simply has to care enough to catch you.

The resources are staggering for the governmental agencies —and even for the private citizens—for there are sophisticated electronic, photographic, and other surveillance equipment; paid snoopers; informers; giant computer banks; and—for government use only—warrants, the legal system, and the psychological power of being Official.

But shed no tears for the private snooper because he hasn't the use of warrants or the legal system, for the government doesn't always use them either. They only get in the way of a really clandestine operation.

Special skill is not required for the use of the electronic gadgets. Nor do you have to be rich to possess them. They're not quite as easy to buy as the morning paper—but almost. And they come in an intriguing variety of disguises, if the snooper wants to get fancy about it: There are cuff links and belt buckles, tie clasps and cigarette lighters. One might be found in your drink (the infamous olive transmitter), fed to your dog, or nailed into your wall.

A thoughtful acquaintance could give you a gift, a beautifully decorative table lamp. Called the Whisper Light, and available from a number of suppliers, it is actually a transmitter, functioning whether it is turned on or off, plugged in, left bulbless in a closet, dismantled, or stored away for good. Hours of listening pleasure with a tuner and tape recorder will delight your generous acquaintance, while you tell secrets that are "just between you and me and the bedpost."

Your dog isn't safe, either. An FM transmitter, smaller than an aspirin tablet, can be easily slipped into your faithful pet's lunch. It generates its own electrical power from the animal's body heat for about six hours, when—despite its inventiveness—it is necessarily eliminated. And it will not be affected by the noise of Fido's stomach growling.

Most of us, with even a smattering of legal knowledge, gleaned from summaries of Supreme Court decisions in the newspapers, still think we are protected from all of these clever little eavesdropping devices. Actually in a legal sense we are. The last decision concerning the use of covert electronic surveillance handed down by the Supreme Court in 1973 refined and narrowed the circumstances under which bugging and wiretapping can be employed. It was the latest in a series of such decisions reaching back over the last thirty years, which reaffirmed, in somewhat hazy terms, the constitutional prohibition against the seizure of evidence without a warrant. But those hazy terms did leave one large hole, that being in those cases of "national security" surveillance. Watergate brought this particular aspect of non-court ordered wiretapping to the forefront, and although Nixon's third Attorney General Elliot Richardson stated that he would try to make certain that a "genuine national security interest" was present before ordering future wiretaps without court orders, it seemed to echo the same criteria which the Nixon Administration had used when four newsmen and thirteen high Government officials were bugged under the "national security" umbrella. (Although since Mr. Richardson attained a legendary "saintliness" with his dramatic resignation, he has often spoken of a need to secure privacy with much stricter regulation of electronic surveillance. He is right, of course, for as William B. Saxbe, Nixon's fourth Attorney General pointed out in a 1974 news conference, the Attorney General himself is the only safeguard against excessive tapping. He mentioned that fact after having pointed out that he had approved requests for three "national security" wiretaps in his first week on the job.)

In any case, Supreme Court decisions, Federal Communications Commission regulations, and past executive orders are often ignored, and tapping is still a burgeoning business replete with "new lines" and improved techniques.

The most interesting device for tapping a telephone, though, is still the old reliable "harmonica bug," which was invented in the early sixties by an electronics wizard from Lower Manhattan, Emanuel Mittleman.

The harmonica bug uses the telephone itself as the power source, thus insuring virtually permanent transmission (barring disconnection of the telephone or discovery of the bug.) A professional could be in and out of your office in less than five minutes; thereafter all he has to do is dial your telephone number, blow into a specially tuned harmonica, which stops your phone from ringing and activates the bug, and listen. Even when your telephone is in the cradle, it is a microphone transmitting anything in the room —from private business meetings to personal conversations.

Many such devices are readily available to the private citizen, and the government can also draw on an almost unlimited supply of highly developed devices available only to federal, state, and local agencies and accredited private detective firms.

If they don't want to listen, they can always watch. Infrared light techniques permit a room to be photographed through solid walls. Closed-circuit television and other cameras have also been miniaturized and can be concealed in a room with little chance of discovery. Of course, if you still leave your windows open, or venture outside for a meeting in the park (away from bugged telephones, walls, and lamps), highly developed telescopic cameras can photograph you a thousand yards away.

As anyone who ever followed the exploits of Mike Hammer or Sherlock Holmes knows, shadowing a suspect is a fine art. But even that is changing. Anyone with access to your clothing—your wife, the tailor, the cleaners—can plant a transistorized mike whose homing signal can easily be followed at a safe (and unspottable) distance. If necessary, you could always be fed a mike like your dog. Sometimes six hours is more than enough time to find out your secrets.

And even if the previously given reasons don't fit your particular case, and you still feel relatively safe and secure, there are many more reasons why you might be watched.

You may have applied for a federal housing loan, for example, or be active in labor negotations; civil rights groups; right, center or leftwing political groups; Black Panthers; SDS; John Birch Society; or Society of Friends.

You may have used drugs or have friends who do—even once. Ever visit those friends? Maybe you wrote to your Governor, senator, or congressman, or even to the President of the United States.

You probably didn't make the mistake that Christopher North did, but if you had, you would not have liked the treatment which followed.

Christopher North, it seems, made the mistake of asking United States Transportation Secretary Claude Brinegar if he thought President Nixon should be impeached. Brinegar was touring San Francisco's subway system in May 1973 when North stepped up to him and asked the politically charged question in a calm manner. Brinegar didn't answer and North repeated the question while being pulled away by subway police.

North was arrested for assault and resisting arrest, charged, fingerprinted, and scheduled for trial. Federal charges of assaulting a Cabinet Officer were dropped when the trial judge found the case a waste of time and successfully urged the prosecution to drop it. But by this time, the record and fingerprints of North, a schoolteacher now working for the Postal Service, had been provided to the Board of Education. North's fingerprints, provided by the Board when he applied for a job, matched the prints taken at his arrest. For his public-spirited inquiry, North now has an arrest and fingerprint file at the State Board of Education, the subway police, the Berkeley city police, the state police, possibly the Secret Service and the Postal Service, the FBI in San Francisco and the FBI in Washington, D.C.

North's case is admittedly unique, because most of the recordkeeping on innocent citizens is unknown to those citizens. North has the somewhat dubious advantage of knowing of his records. But the children of migrant workers might not know about their records, nor those who took part in Earth Day celebrations, attended peace marches, or visited the grave of Martin Luther King.

If we still have missed you in specifics, be not dismayed, for there is bound to be a category we missed and you do fit somebody's definition of a "person of interest."

Among the Secret Service guidelines of gathering information on "a person of interest" are these particular ones:

A. Information pertaining to a threat, plan or attempt by an individual, group of any organization to physically harm or embarrass the persons protected by the U.S. Secret Service, or any other high U.S. Government Official at home or abroad.

D. Information on persons who insist upon personally contacting high government officials for the purpose of redress of imaginary grievances, etc.

E. Information on any person who makes oral or written statements about high Government officials in the following categories: (1) threatening statements; (2) irrational statements; and (3) abusive statements.

F. Information on professional gate crashers.

In a speech relating to these August 1970 guidelines, Senator Sam Ervin, Jr. wryly noted, "Although I am not a professional gate-crasher, I am a malcontent on many issues.

"I have written the President and other high officials complaining of grievances that some may consider 'imaginary.' And on occasion I have 'embarrassed' high government officials."

As Senator Ervin concluded, he could well have fit within the scope of the Secret Service's intelligence-gatherers even before his Watergate Investigating Committee embarrassed several high government officials very severely. At that time, 1970, everyone assumed the Senator was ribbing the Secret Service over the impreciseness of the guidelines, but just six months later, Ervin's Subcommittee on Constitutional Rights released testimony that indicated Senator Adlai E. Stevenson 3rd, Representative Abner Mikva, and former Illinois Governor Otto Kerner had all been spied on by the 113th Army Intelligence group in Chicago.

The spy apparatus stretches throughout every agency, the Army, Navy, Air Force, police, credit bureaus, insurance companies, and rival businesses.

If this weren't frightening enough, the burgeoning growth of "immediately retrievable information system" data banks adds the icing to the cake. It insures that once information is obtained, by whatever means, it will remain on file, to be retrieved perhaps years later for uses entirely at odds with the reasons the information was gathered in the first place.

Sam Ervin once said he would like to spread a gospel of his own concerning computer data banks. "It is my belief that while the Recording Angel drops a tear occasionally to wash out the record of our human iniquities, there is no compassion to be found in computers. Nor is it to be found in all the new instruments for measuring man which the behavioral sciences and the new technology hold out to us.

"In other words, a computer has a most remarkable memory, never forgets anything, but it has no heart and it has no forgiveness."

Not only does the computer never forget what you have done, it can also remember things about you which never happened. A careless input operator strikes the wrong key and the information on sexual offender John Smith goes directly into your file. And somewhere in the cold heart of that vast data bank, it says that you expose yourself to little girls.

And you don't even know the information is there. It just sits there and waits until some future time when the keypunch operator types your name out, and rolling out on the tape for all to see is your "record."

But let's assume that whatever information "they" have on you is correct. None of their business, but correct all the same. How did they get it?

Just to give you an idea of how this could happen, let's take the case of an imaginary American family: the Greens.

Howard Green is forty-five, a sports buff, taxpayer (always on time and correct), and homeowner.

Helen, his wife, owns a small shop just outside the city.

Dana, twenty-three, Michael, twenty-one, and David, eighteen, are their three children.

Howard owns his own home in Middle Oaks, thirty-five minutes from down-town Megalopolis, where he works for a small plastics firm. He is well-regarded within his company; in fact, he is being considered for promotion to vice president in charge of production. He's presently ironing out some minor problems with the labor union at the firm. He's been approached by rival companies because of his excellent reputation.

Howard votes in most of the elections, reads the newspapers, and always catches the news on television or radio two or three times a day. In general, he's interested in his environment and national and international issues. He supports the government in most areas of policy.

The only flaw in this fairly normal scene is his secretary, Doris. They're having an affair.

Helen's shop specializes in ceramics, most of which she creates herself. Helen is fiercely independent—the shop is completely hers, and woe to Howard if he dares interfere. Cruising along on the area's new fad for ceramics, Helen's shop is finally making a profit—rather modest, but a profit. Only her bookkeeping leaves a little to be desired.

Their children are all pretty active. Dana is a saleswoman in a large department store. David is a student at an out-of-state college. Michael is two years into a three-year Army hitch and is stationed nearby. He takes advantage of the windfall and spends weekends at home.

Most would agree that the Greens seem like an ordinary family. Unfortunately for their privacy, however, several government agencies, three private detectives, and assorted other snoopers don't seem to think them very ordinary at all.

Their phones are bugged, their mail opened and perused, there are still photos, movies, and bulging dossiers about the private activities of each family member. The reason:

Helen owes money to the IRS, thanks to her bad bookkeeping. As a result, her office and home phones are bugged, her bank records have been studied by agents, and her private mail has been intercepted en route. All this for $1,763.68 she owes in back taxes.

Howard can't escape surveillance, either. If he's not overheard using his home telephone by Helen's IRS tap, he can always use his tapped office phone. The radio receiver is in the office of the president of his company. He doesn't promote just anybody—it's important, he feels, to know just what kind of man you're making a vice president.

If he avoids his phones and works instead, the company executives can always listen in on the labor negotiations being held in secret. The conference room is bugged.

"It is surprising," one executive remarked, "what men say to each other in the washroom. Discontent among employees can be stopped before they really become a problem, and we learn about pilfering of company property that way." So it is not surprising that if Howard seeks privacy in the men's room, that too is bugged.

In case Howard decides simply to stop talking and thereby escape surveillance, two people make sure he's watched during the working hours and during the private ones.

A company spy, just down the hall from Howard's office, is watching everyone with access to blueprints that have been strangely landing in a rival's hands. Howard, of course, is in charge of the blueprints.

And when he leaves the company, a private detective hired by a rival company picks up the trail. They want to hire Howard with a substantial raise in salary and responsibilities. First, of course, they want to know a little more about the private life of the man they're getting. "When we hire the man, we hire the wife," an executive commented. Helen is watched by the same detective.

Dana works next to another company spy, this one looking for employee pilferage. There are thirteen closed-circuit TV cameras throughout the store. The dressing rooms are fitted with two-way mirrors. The restrooms are bugged, and a bimonthly lie-detector test is required of all employees.

Michael is in Army Intelligence, a job which requires little more than pencil-pushing as a glorified file clerk. Yet before he was even allowed this desultory activity, his entire background was checked out in detail. Friends, neighbors, teachers, and acquaintances were all questioned about his character, beliefs, and associates. All of this information on Michael and his family is on tape. Retrievable at the push of the computer button. His fingerprints were automatically sent to Washington when he entered the Army. They are on file for life. Probably longer.

Unfortunately, Michael recently talked to a friend who attended a meeting of the American Serviceman's Union. This heinous crime resulted in censored mail, monitored phone calls, and a twenty-four-hour tail. Complete with photographs and movies, all courtesy of U.S. Army Intelligence.

David, the college student, holds the family surveillance record. Not only is all the information about his physical and psychological states of health, collected when he enrolled at the school, on file there: he also has his own folder at the Army's Counter Intelligence Analysis Branch (CIAB), which subscribes to the underground newspaper for which he once wrote an article. His arrest record (suspicion of burglary—a nonsense charge dismissed for lack of evidence) is in four dossiers. The peace march he attended landed him in the files of the American Security Council, a private watchdog organization with ultrarightwing leanings. If he ever wants to land a job after his Army service, he better not apply to one of the companies to which the ASC passes its information.

Two of David's friends, "known users of marijuana and hashish," helped him establish his record. Now he's under surveillance by the Bureau of Narcotics and Dangerous Drugs. There are 125 photographs of David with the "suspects."

Unbelievable? Not really. There are cases on record that make the Greens' surveillance look like Amateur Night. And their case, though hypothetical, is terrifyingly possible.

Daniel Schorr, a television newsman, was tailed, photographed, and bugged for months by the government. When it was finally discovered, the White House smugly announced that Mr. Schorr was simply under consideration for a high-level governmental position and was being "routinely investigated."

Maybe some of us, looking over our shoulders at the secret police, might smile exultingly in the knowledge that we're about to be offered a wonderful job at the White House. Most of us, though, will shudder in the chilling wind from the future, and cringe under the darkening shadow of Big Brother.

Almost the only way, it seems, that anyone can escape some kind of data-gathering about his private life is by living alone away from all human activity as a hermit. And then some human behavioral scientist who wishes to record an abnormal life will probably be watching from behind the bushes with a pair of binoculars.

The following chapters will—we hope—help you understand the present danger of the privacy invaders in all of their various disguises, and give you some ideas about what you can and should do next.

That is, if you care about protecting your own personal privacy.

Introduction

by Nat Hentoff

Among Justice Louis Brandeis's many virtues was a kind of prescience, a finely attuned alertness to prospective dangers to individual liberties. In 1928, for example, a majority of the Supreme Court declared a form of electronic secret surveillance, then in its technological infancy, to be constitutional. The particular incursion on the right of privacy at issue in the case (*Olmstead v. United States*) was wiretapping.

Writing in dissent, Justice Brandeis emphasized that "The makers of our Constitution conferred, as against the Government, the right to be let alone—the most comprehensive of rights and the right most valued by civilized men."

Brandeis not prevailing, the head of the camel—to use a metaphor of Justice William O. Douglas in another case—was in the tent. Since then, as the technology of surveillance has advanced geometrically and as government officials and their agents—along with non-governmental shredders of privacy working for credit-rating, insurance and other firms—have become accustomed to collecting all sorts of data about citizens, this "right most valued by civilized men" has been steadily eroded.

We are now at a stage in which the following grim analysis by Alexander Solzhenitsyn in "Cancer Ward" applies as well to our own psychic terrain even though we live in a constitutional democracy:

"As every man goes through life, he fills in a number of forms for the record, each containing a number of questions . . . There are thus hundreds of little threads in all. If these threads were suddenly to become visible, the whole sky would look like a spider's web

. . . They are not visible, they are not material, but every man is constantly aware of their existence . . . Each man, permanently aware of his own invisible threads, naturally develops a respect for the people who manipulate the threads."

This invisible spider web is the subject of NO PLACE TO HIDE by Alan LeMond and Ron Fry, a comprehensive exploration of the gathering forces in this country which, unless checked by legislation and continual monitoring by civil liberties organizations, will create so pervasive a web to which each of us is tied that, as Justice Douglas has warned, "Our citizens will be afraid to utter any but the safest and most orthodox thoughts, afraid to associate with any but the most acceptable people. Freedom as the Constitution envisages (it) will have vanished."

If this prophecy appears to you to have more to do with the hyperbole of paranoia than with reality, you are now in for a knowledge shock because LeMond and Fry, through careful and overwhelming documentation, have made a vital contribution to our constitutional welfare—if only enough of the citizenry heed and act on the alarm they have sounded that privacy has become a most endangered species.

I come to this book with a background on the subject which encompasses some thirty years of reporting on privacy and more than a decade of work against its violators as a Board Member of the New York Civil Liberties Union committees. Also, with Paul Cowan and Nick Egleson, I am co-author of a 1974 book, *State Secrets: Police Surveillance in America* (Holt, Rinehart and Winston).

Although I thought I knew the field quite well, there is much in NO PLACE TO HIDE—the sections on technology and on the Internal Revenue Service, for instance—which has markedly and usefully added to my knowledge.

I do not intend to paraphrase LeMond's and Fry's findings in this introduction—each section is too richly detailed for that in any case—but instead want to indicate that the dangers to privacy they examine have not in the least diminished in post-Watergate America. Granted that the Nixon Administration was the most contemptuous of the Bill of Rights of any in American history; nonetheless, *every* Administration in this century has, in one way or another, tried to find out more about various citizens than it had any constitutional right to. The FBI's activities in this regard—including the "black bag" operations referred to in this book—have proliferated under both Democratic and Republican Presidents.

Simultaneously, no Administration has been moved—so far anyway—to counter the swiftly accelerating privacy invasions of such non-government operations as the Retail Credit Co. which, with headquarters in Atlanta, has files on the personal lives of 45-million Americans and the capacity of reporting credit information on 98 percent of the population.

It is true that finally, some members of Congress, among them Edward Koch (one of those to whom this book is dedicated) have filed and have moved to get support for legislation intended to curb both governmental and private assaults on our right "to be let alone." As of this writing, the auguries are that some form of privacy legislation is likely to be passed; but even if that highly desirable development does occur, there are more than sufficient loopholes in the prospective bills to assure the need to press for ever tighter legislation in the years to come.

Furthermore, there is no sign that most law-enforcement officials have yet experienced a radical change of consciousness with regard to *their* constitutional responsibility to respect individual privacy. And without that change of consciousness, legislation protecting privacy can be evaded—unless there is constant vigilance by both Congress and citizens' groups. For all the surface differences between J. Edgar Hoover and current FBI Director Clarence Kelly, for instance, I am not convinced that the latter's devotion to the Bill of Rights is any more fervent than his predecessor's, particularly since Clarence Kelly declared on

September 6, 1974, that he considers FBI wiretapping for "political" reasons to be "legal" and "justified."

Nor does the present composition of the Supreme Court insure much confidence that the Bill of Rights is safe from being mugged there. Richard Nixon's most lasting legacy are his four appointees to the Court, the youngest of whom, William Rehnquist, as LeMond and Fry point out, told Senator Sam Ervin before he was confirmed that it would not be a violation of the Senator's rights and liberties if the government were to put him under secret surveillance.

Only an informed and acutely concerned citizenry, in sum, can protect its privacy—by expressing its will politically, using as a fundamental criterion for voting the degree of sensitivity of each candidate to the need to safeguard individual liberties. Even the Supreme Court would pay heed to those kinds of election returns.

The key problem, as of now, is stated in this book by Jerome Weisner, president of MIT: "I doubt that anyone is aware of the full extent of surveillance and information collection activities that go on in this country."

Accordingly, NO PLACE TO HIDE—with its remarkable scope of exactly such information—ought to be widely circulated throughout the political spectrum. For privacy is as much a conservative as a liberal issue. Along with Ed Koch, for example, one of the most effective Congressmen in devising and working for privacy legislation has been Barry Goldwater, Jr.

In speeches throughout the country before groups which liberals do not usually get to address, Barry Goldwater, Jr. has been stressing that "There are currently 150,000 computers in use in the United States, and some 350,000 remote-data terminals (to which the computers are connected). Predictions have been made indicating there will be 250,000 computers and 800,000 terminals by 1975. It is possible today to build a computerized on-line file containing the compact equivalent of 20 pages of typed information about the personal history and selected activities of every man, woman and child in the United States. In this system, any single record can be retrieved in about 30 seconds. Few can deny that we are approaching a data bank society.''

Like LeMond and Fry, Goldwater, Jr. understands a corollary danger of a data bank society. In many faced with such highly sophisticated technology, a feeling of impotency begins to grow. With such pervasively swift technology, the thesis goes, it is just no longer possible to protect individual privacy. This is a delusion, and a dangerous one, even when prompted by such an otherwise brilliant analyst of society as Jacques Ellul.

The truth—as continually underlined by Francis Sargent, former governor of Massachusetts and a dauntless defender of the right of privacy—is that "The computer itself is not the danger. It is the ethic of the computer—the idea that man can be dealt with in the aggregate; that there are only groups out there, not individuals." Or as Barry Goldwater, Jr. puts it, "My objective is not to undo or slow down technical advancement, but rather to put men *over* machines."

It is not computers but men, or women, who set such policies to gather information to be fed into the computer such as the following (disclosed in a letter to me in April, 1974):

"Recently, I was serving on a Federal jury. During some free time, I attempted to enter, as a spectator, the trial of a black militant accused of murder. I was asked for identification. (Since I wore a suit, they didn't 'sweep' me with a 'beeper' device).

"Before I knew what was happening, the marshal noted my name and address in a log he kept of all spectators. It was only after I entered the courtroom that I realized my name was likely going to be fed to the Great Computer as 'Spectator at a Trial of a Black Militant,' "

On what constitutional ground does a marshal keep a record of citizens engaging in their right to attend a public trial? There is no such constitutional ground, and the practice should be stopped.

Similarly, the computer cannot be blamed for the not uncommon unpleasant surprise suffered in 1971 by a woman living in Croton-on-Hudson, New York. She received a letter from Nationwide Insurance ("The man from Nationwide is on your side") canceling her auto insurance policy. There was a P.S.: "This action was influenced by information in a consumer report made at our request by Retail Credit Co., White Plains, N.Y. office, a reliable and reputable source of information for business decisions."

What could this "reliable" source of information have turned up on a woman who had never been in an auto accident and had never been late with an insurance payment? She found out—through the intervention of the American Civil Liberties Union. Retail Credit had told the insurance company that the woman's son was a "hippie-type" who was "suspected" of using drugs.

The boy in question, a non-drug-user, had been voted the student "who did the most for Croton-Harmon High." According to his principal, he was "a model student." The boy had even been active in the PTA!

What went wrong with this "reputable" source of information? As LeMond and Fry reveal in NO PLACE TO HIDE, what went wrong is the pressure these "information" gathering firms place on their investigators. Retail Credit according to J. Thomas Rosch, director of the Federal Trade Commission Bureau of Consumer Protection, pays its investigators in such a way that "a premium is out on the *number* of daily reports gathered—at the expense of their accuracy."

Nor can advancing technology be blamed for another outrage, reported by the American Civil Liberties Union (a report that also shows what kinds of counter-action can be taken against this form of privacy-invasion):

"A three-pronged attack is planned by the Cleveland chapter of the ACLU against a local company which placed a bugging device in the ladies' washroom in hopes of overhearing union organizers during negotiations. Die-Cut Products forced female employees to notify their foreman before visiting the bathroom so that individual voices could be readily identified. One of the workers noticed the bug, photographed it, then notified the police, who confiscated the illegal device. Now Die-Cut Products is facing a civil suit from the ACLU, a criminal prosecution from the state's attorney, and administrative action by the National Labor Relations Board. The Cleveland ACLU chapter's 1984 Committee took the unusual step of moving against a private company because "today many companies have acquired the means and the technology to threaten civil liberties.''

So they have, and those companies as well as government—on all levels—have to be exposed when its agents act as if this were *not* a constitutional democracy. And as Congress becomes more aware of the ubiquitous assaults on privacy throughout industry and government, its members have to be shown that the electorate not only supports privacy legislation but also insists on more of it. One way, incidentally, of prodding your Congressman is to send him a copy of NO PLACE TO HIDE.

By the time you finish this book, I expect that you yourself will have come to agree with Professor Arthur Miller, a Harvard Law School expert on privacy, who maintains that if large numbers of us do not awaken "to the danger of information abuse," we may reach a time, not too many years from now, when we discover, too late, "that the mantle of policy-making is being worn by specially trained technicians who have found time to master the machine and are manipulating it for their own purposes. If we then have a dictatorship of dossiers and data banks rather than of hobnailed boots, it will not be any less a dictatorship.''

—January, 1975

Chapter One:

A Brief Background
on the Bug

*"The right of the people to be secure in their persons,
houses and effects, and against unreasonable searches
and seizures, shall not be violated, and no warrants
shall issue, but upon probable cause, supported by oath
or affirmation, and particularly describing the place to
be searched, and the person or things to be seized."*
—Fourth Amendment to the United States Constitution

The very thought of electronic surveillance of any kind used
surreptitiously, for whatever reason, is terrifying and maddening
enough, but think about that smug little phrase: "I've got nothing
to hide." How would you feel if you knew that were actually true?
You have nothing to hide, because they already know all about
you.

Ina and Morton H. Halperin know that feeling well. The phone
in their Maryland home was bugged for a period not less than eight
and possibly as long as twenty-two months beginning in May
1969. It was bugged when Mr. Halperin was on the staff of the
National Security Council in that year. It was bugged without his
consent and without a court order. In fact, the Halperins learned
about it through a fluke. Daniel Ellsberg happened to use their

phone and was overheard. This overheard conversation of Ellsberg's was reported to the presiding judge at the Los Angeles Pentagon Papers trial and was a contributing factor in the abrupt ending of the trial.

"But for us the trials have just begun," the Halperins stated in an article appearing on the Op-Ed page of the New York *Times*. What, they wondered, had been overheard? All the conversations of their sons, then aged three, five, and seven? Calls to a grandmother in New York? To the butcher? To the babysitter? From the obscene caller who was bothering them at the time?

"What else did the summaries [those presented for Kissinger and John Ehrlichman to read] contain? If there was no classified information, then surely there was amidst the everyday conversations and gossip, our political views stated frankly and privately to close friends.

"We are outraged because not only were our words intercepted but also those of the many people who spoke to us on the phone. Most of them have no connection with the Government or access to national security information. They, too, have cause to feel outraged."

The Halperins were righteously indignant. And why not? Isn't—as the Halperins asked in their article—a genuine national security based on a respect by the government for the rights of the people? Instead of being based on the fear of a government overhearing everything that is said?

(On April 1, 1974, Morton Halperin was granted "discovery" of all government documents in his damage suit—*Halperin* v. *Kissinger* CA 1187-73, D.D.C. Such discovery is a rarity in "national security" tap cases.)

What in the name of national security is going on?

Such noble sentiments as those expressed in the Fourth Amendment are not the pipe dreams of some utopian dreamers. They are practical safeguards devised for the protection of the citizens against the universal tendencies of governments to try to contain, control, or nullify the opposition, to place the masses into manipulable positions like so many pawns on a chessboard. It makes for greater efficiency, you know, but it sure does cut down on individual liberty and our "inherent rights."

One of the most blatant infringements on the rights of American citizens "to be secure in their persons, houses, papers, and effects" is the use of electronic surveillance, whether by tapping the wires of the telephone (as was used on the Halperins), or by implanting bugs—the tiny microphones and transmitters mentioned earlier—in walls, furniture, or clothing.

And that infringement is practiced not only by the government, but by practically every type of business and private citizen. "Everybody wants to snoop on his brother; you know—I am my brother's snooper," says Ben Jamil, president of the now-defunct Continental Telephone Supply Company.

Continental Telephone Supply was typical of the manufacturers and distributors of electronic surveillance equipment that flourished in the last decade. They sold everything. From cheap, easy-to-install telephone recording devices and wireless transmitters for the amateur to sophisticated and complex gear for the professionals of the trade. Full-page advertisements in the New York *Times* insured a steady stream of amateur sleuths, private investigators, criminals, and the plain curious into Continental's showrooms.

Whatever laws there were protecting the privacy of individuals from unwarranted and unwanted surveillance, or hindering the sale of electronic devices, were easily subverted by the many electronic firms dealing in such items. In fact, until the Justice Department cracked down on such blatantly illegal behavior, anyone at all could simply walk into Continental's showroom on Manhattan's West Forty-Sixth Street and buy whatever struck his fancy, whether legal, shadily legal, or technically illegal.

The advertisements for the incredibly varied array of private invasion equipment, were so cute and ambiguous that only a child, and a rather naive one, could possibly misunderstand their true intent. Consider one of Continental's ads in a 1967 catalogue:

Presenting the most modern and efficient attaché case. Containing a voice activated recording system, starts when there are voices, shuts off when there is silence; concealed microphone; nature lovers can record bird and animal sounds undetected.

Naturally, hundreds of avid nature-lovers rushed to Continental's display cases to purchase their own recorders, no doubt dreaming of nights in the forest, listening enraptured to their undetected attaché case as it zeroed in on the mating call of the yellow-breasted hornswoggle. The attaché cases did—in some instances—wind up in unusual places: bedrooms, meeting rooms, closets, restaurant booths, etc.—but who are we to question the eccentric ways of the nation's birdwatchers?

(A manufacturer of wireless transmitters in 1973 must have remembered the advertisement. When asked what his device was used for, he characterized them as mere toys: "For bird watchers. It will pick up the sounds of birds in the backyard and transfer the sound to an FM frequency." Nature is evidently big business for the electronics manufacturers. Whoever suspected that the ranks of the nation's birdwatchers and assorted nature-lovers had grown so vast or so technologically subtle?)

Most of us, reading and hearing about the increasing supplies of miniaturized transmitters, concealed microphones, wiretaps, infrared photographic equipment ("sees through walls; amuse your friends with pictures they didn't even know were being taken!"), shotgun mikes, etc., should not have been bowled over by the splash of front-page headlines relating the blatant use of electronic equipment in recent years. Yet most of us were. Why? What made us so innocent? There is a long, long history behind bugging and wiretapping with electronic equipment, stretching back further than even John Dean could remember.

The May 17, 1916, New York *Times* reported: "The Thompson Committee investigating public utilities heard yesterday that the police of New York have been tapping telephone wires by wholesale, and the Committee will begin today an investigation of the entire subject. An officer of the New York Telephone Company told Senator Thompson that in the past two years 350 telephone wires have been officially tapped by the police.

"According to information furnished to the Committee, telephone wiretapping was begun back in 1895, when William L. Strong was Mayor. Through succeeding city administrations, the practice has prevailed and grown."

Although Congressman George Loft of New York demanded further and more detailed investigations of the entire range of snooping going on, the entry of the United States into World War I postponed any serious questioning of the wiretapping epidemic in New York. However, wiretapping was banned for the duration of the war.

By the end of the war, a new government organization, already ten years old, was ready to begin its own surveillance career under a newly appointed director, the young, fire-breathing law-enforcement official named J. Edgar Hoover.

The scope of the FBI's surveillance under the direction of J. Edgar is only now beginning to come out. Previously, people such as Allen Dulles (once director of the CIA) wrote and spoke such blatant pap as this statement from his book, *The Craft of Intelligence*: "Our government, by its very nature—and our open society in all its instincts under the Constitution and the Bill of Rights—automatically outlaws intelligence organizations of the kind that have developed in police states."

It is difficult to believe that Mr. Dulles was not aware of the scope of the activities of the Federal Bureau of Investigation, activities which were probably as secretive and terrifying in all of their multitudinous aspects as that "of the kind that have developed in police states."

Few people had any idea of the influence that the FBI exerted on the country until after Hoover's death and the revelations of the Watergate inquiry. The 1971 break-in and looting of the FBI field office in Media, Pennsylvania, shocked millions of newspaper readers, it is true. But in 1971, most of the country had too many other things to worry about—the war, the various protests, the beginnings of our now-rampant inflation—to be too concerned about even the severely edited contents of the purloined files. There was not heard over the land of the free any collective audible protest from the people—not even a sigh. And a protest must be heard if any change in government policy is to be made. The Vietnam War is an obvious example.

The only previous occurrence that allowed the average citizen even the briefest glimpse into the inner workings of this vast bureaucratic investigative machine had been in 1949, when Judith Coplon, an employee of the Justice Department, was arrested and tried for passing top-secret FBI files to Russian agents. It was brought out that there had been forty FBI agents monitoring her private conversations.

The Bureau is, was, and probably ever shall be the largest user of wiretaps and bugging devices (unless another White House plumbing operation is set up) in the federal bureaucracy. Following World War I, and the appointment of Hoover as director in 1924, the Attorney General outlawed wiretapping. Hoover was not in the least bothered by the ban since, at the time, he thought wiretapping a "cowardly" way to do business. The ban was reaffirmed in 1928 under President Coolidge.

However, the ban exempted the Bureau of Prohibition, probably due to the difficulty of enforcing an impossible law, anyway, so it was necessary to take every advantage available.

The use of wiretapping by this bureau to break a large and inordinately well-publicized bootlegging operation gave rise to what was to become the now-famous Olmsteid case (1928). In its decision, the Supreme Court ruled that evidence "secured by use of the sense of hearing and that only" was constitutionally obtained, and thus valid. It was not an "unreasonable search or seizure" as the terms were understood in the Fourth Amendment.

That ruling was not a unanimous one, however. Justice Brandeis, in a famous dissent, remarked acidly that "as a means of espionage, writs of assistance and general warrants are but puny instruments of tyranny and oppression when compared with wiretapping."

Justice Holmes, echoing Brandeis's fear of laying the groundwork for rampant government-sponsored spying on private citizens, added that "it is better sometimes that crime should go unpunished than that the citizen should be liable to have his privacy invaded, his desks broken into, private books, letters and papers exposed to prying curiosity, and to the misconstruction of ignorant and suspicious persons."

Attorney General William D. Mitchell—acting much as the recent Attorney General Mitchell probably would have in similar circumstances—did little to ease the fears of Justices Brandeis and Holmes. He immediately issued instructions allowing the installation of wiretaps at "the personal direction of the Chief of the Bureau involved." Despite attempts by both the seventy-first and seventy-second Congresses to outlaw wiretapping, little was accomplished, except to stir Mitchell to propose legislative countermoves to remove the bar on FBI wiretapping altogether. The Congresses did accomplish a very minor victory by attaching a rider to the Department of Justice Appropriation Act for 1933, which prohibited the use of wiretapping in relation to prohibition. When prohibition died soon thereafter, so did the enthusiasm of the congressional anti-wiretapping lobby.

The Federal Communications Act of 1934 did seem to repair —at least at first glance—the gaping hole left in the dike. Section 605 specifically forbade the interception or disclosure of interstate telephone messages, though it stopped short of banning the actual act of wiretapping.

Essentially, all Section 605 amounted to was an instruction to the government that while wiretapping was fine, don't ever let anyone know that you've done it. This, of course, could and did lead to problems. But the impossibility of a defense attorney's proving that a "confidential informant" was, in reality, an electronic eavesdropping device, didn't seem to faze the honorable legislators.

Despite the act, and despite subsequent Supreme Court decisions which significantly narrowed the right to wiretap, and despite his own earlier arguments against the practice, Hoover's FBI began wiretapping as early as the late 1930s.

The true extent of the Bureau's surge into electronic surveillance may eventually be known, but no statistics have as yet been forthcoming from either the Bureau or the Department of Justice.

Bugs were evidently used with even less discretion and less respect for the letter of the law then than they were in the 1960s and 1970s. According to recent disclosures, microphone surveillance in this era didn't even require the director's approval, which meant that a Special Agent in Charge had sole power over the use of hidden microphones. Both wiretapping and bugging were carried out without any real legal authority. But again a war came along to change the habits of government surveillance experts.

World War II brought the threat of foreign espionage to the United States and changed the entire nature of surveillance conducted in the prewar days. What was not legal, although practiced prewar, became legal during the war. It, of course, was all done in the name of national security.

An executive order issued by President Roosevelt in June, 1939 put the FBI in charge of all espionage investigation and security. A further presidential order that September directed all the other law-enforcement agencies to consider the FBI the sole seat of power for surveillance over espionage activities, and instructed them to turn any and all information on espionage, counterespionage, sabotage, and subversive acts over to the Bureau.

Fascist and Communist saboteurs lurked behind every bush and locked door, according to Hoover's public relations press. And the previous difference between foreign enemies and domestic puppets of foreign governments disappeared swiftly. So did the difference between the surveillance of foreigners and domestics.

The FBI could conceivably spy on just about anyone. After all, those foreign agents were everywhere, and . . . because someone appeared on the surface to be just another innocent and patriotic citizen was no reason to believe it was true, was it? A vague concept of "the greater good" prevailed over any active suspicions of unlimited and unchecked domestic surveillance by a national police force.

As Attorney General Robert Jackson put it in 1940, the FBI had to maintain "steady surveillance over individuals and groups within the United States who are so sympathetic with the system or designs of foreign dictators as to make them a likely source of federal law violation."

The designation of a person as "a likely source of federal law violation" is one of the first signs that a baby Big Brother is attempting his first steps. In fact, the basic difference between a legitimate investigation and an illegal surveillance can be found in this phrase. For an investigation presupposes that there is something going on, while surveillance, used with the justification for watching "just in case," is something else again.

But it was wartime in 1940. The whole world was committing violations of human rights. That's a part of war. And also seeds of future violations are sown during wars. Unintentionally, probably. In the name of national security, certainly.

And national security was the probable reason behind FDR's further move to insure the evolution of the FBI into, for all intents and purposes, a superexecutive national police organization. His memorandum to Attorney General Jackson on May 21, 1940, overturned not only the ban Jackson had imposed on wiretapping only one hundred days before, but also the rules of all his presidential predecessors since 1924. Roosevelt wrote:

> You are therefore authorized and directed in such cases
> as you may approve, after investigation of the need in
> each case, to authorize the necessary investigating
> agents that they are at liberty to secure information by

listening devices directed to the conversation or other communications of persons suspected of subversive activities against the government of the United States, including suspected spies. You are requested furthermore to limit these investigations so conducted to a minimum and to limit them, insofar as possible, to aliens.

This memo became the sole authority for electronic surveillance during World War II. Interpreting the term "listening device" to mean *only* a wiretap, Hoover continued to install bugs without anyone's approval. And whenever he did want a wiretap, he simply asked the Attorney General—whose authorization was immediately forthcoming.

And so the growing investigatory bureaucracy, reporting only to its director, and its director reporting only to God, had begun its inexorable and seemingly inevitable climb to the heights of unlimited and unchecked power on a national scale.

President Truman added further power to Hoover's personal fiefdom, for he not only extended FDR's wiretapping directive, he also expanded it. All cases of "domestic security" were, under his direction, included.

To be fair to Truman, he may not have been totally aware of what he had done, for this particular expansion was obtained by a tricky Attorney General, Tom Clark. The new head of the Justice Department, under Truman, quoted only the first part of FDR's memo when he sent a message to the President requesting an extension and expansion. Calculatingly missing was the plea to limit "these investigations so conducted to a minimum and to limit them insofar as possible to aliens." Clark was a strong wiretapping proponent, and no doubt omitted the sentence intentionally. Therefore, Truman may have broken new surveillance ground without knowing it. Or at least without being immediately aware of his predecessor's intent in the original order.

And things hummed along nicely on the wiretapping scene under Attorney General Clark with only minor interference along the way. True, when it was disclosed in 1949 that Judith Coplon—the spy who got caught cold—had been monitored by no less than forty FBI agents, there was a minor storm of protest raised, but nothing really changed. Clark made an announcement to the effect that Roosevelt's policy was still being followed to the letter and nothing new had been added. The public seemed mollified by this blatant lie—of course, the public didn't know it was a lie.

Clark's successor as Attorney General, J. Howard McGrath, continued the policy set up by his predecessor but tried to dissuade the FBI from illegal entry to install hidden microphones. His 1952 memorandum instructing the Bureau to cease and desist was —according to subsequent Bureau actions—ignored.

And then when the Eisenhower Administration came into power, Hoover finally—from somewhere and somebody—got specific authority to approve the installation of wiretaps and bugs in the interest of internal security or national safety. Just who that somebody was that gave the go-ahead, though, was never adequately explained, nor was it explained when the ruling went into effect or when it expired. But this ghostly "authority" nevertheless was the sole extralegal basis for FBI eavesdropping for fifteen years.

Then in 1968, the Omnibus Crime Control and Safe Streets Act made bugging legal. Any departmental directives from the Attorney General meant little at this point, and congressional inquiries that might have blossomed were nipped in the bud, and the public outcries for legislation were stifled or resulted in the secretive continuance of the status quo.

Robert Kennedy was more pro-wiretapping than many of his predecessors. It was he who approved the tapping of Dr. Martin Luther King's hotel-suite telephone, supposedly to protect the good doctor from Communist party members in his group. So, of course, Kennedy was aware of the FBI wiretaps on King. He wasn't aware of the FBI bugs. He didn't ask. And Hoover never told.

Katzenbach, Kennedy's successor, asked, however, and was told. Hoover gave him a rundown on the full extent of the Bureau's bugging activities and contended that to outlaw it would doom the Justice Department's fledgling war on organized crime (which Hoover had taken thirty years to acknowledge). The compromise they worked out was supposed to lead to a gradual phasing out of such surveillance, and the Attorney General was thereafter to be informed of any planted bugs the same way he was informed about wiretaps—beforehand.

President Johnson's June 1965 directive, standing firmly behind his Attorney General, prohibited bugs except in national security cases and limited their use to the Department of Justice, of which the FBI was nominally a part.

The tax-evasion case of Fred R. Black, associate of the infamous Bobby Baker, reminded the American public that despite laws, directives, statutes, Supreme Court decisions, and a (false) sense of public security, electronic surveillance was alive and well and living in Washington, D.C. Once again, the ever-faithful FBI was right in there with both feet, admitting it had bugged Black's hotel suite "around the time" the tax evasion case was in progress.

The Solicitor General, Thurgood Marshall—now Supreme Court Justice—insisted that the eavesdropping was incidental and did not relate to the case at hand. Fred Black's attorney—whose supposedly privileged conversations with his client had been ignominiously and painstakingly noted, recorded and transcribed—was not as blasé about it all as the Solicitor General was. He moved for a dismissal, and won.

Case after case followed in which previous convictions were duly overturned and new trials ordered, because of previously undisclosed governmental eavesdropping involved. Ramsey Clark, Johnson's Acting Attorney General at the time, immediately instructed every U.S. Attorney to delay all prosecutions until evidence obtained through the use of illegal bugs was removed completely from the prosecution's presentation.

On June, 16, 1967, he issued a detailed statement of governmental policy with regard to wiretapping and bugging. He noted that wiretapping had already been banned by a presidential directive, but that federal law did not specifically ban wiretapping. (He was speaking of Section 605). The law prohibited only the divulgence of information gathered from taps. He further remarked that a test case had never been introduced in the Supreme Court to test the constitutionality of nontrespassory eavesdropping (planting bugs without actually illegally entering the premises). But Clark nevertheless agreed that it was possible to interpret the safeguards of the Fourth Amendment in such a way that *any* eavesdropping on private conversations was unconstitutional.

When Clark's statement was finished, it seemed—under close examination—to be doubletalk. For the legal loopholes in Section 605, and the fact that a test case had not yet been introduced to the Supreme Court, left the statement without any real substance.

The Supreme Court had tried, it appeared, to close the glaring holes in the fabric of the laws as far back as the Olmsteid decision of 1928, in which the Court declared that "the makers of our Constitution conferred as against the Government, the right to be let alone—the most comprehensive right and the right most valued by civilized man," but the negative decision left a lot to be desired by privacy lovers.

A later decision, *Katz* v. *United States* (389 U.S. 347) reaffirmed this right but overruled the previous decision's finding that indiscriminate warrantless wiretapping was constitutionally legal. The *Katz* decision authorized wiretappings, but only after a legal warrant had been issued by a court: The government's "activities in electronically listening to and recording the petitioner's words violated the privacy on which he justifiably relied . . . and thus constituted a 'search and seizure' within the meaning of the Fourth Amendment."

Justice Stewart tried to prevent further misunderstanding by stressing that ". . . this court has emphasized [over and over again] that the mandate of the [Fourth] Amendment requires adherence to judicial process and that searches conducted outside the judicial process, without prior approval by judges or magistrates, are per se unreasonable under the Fourth Amendment."

Another Supreme Court decision, *Berger v. New York* (388 U.S. 41), even further enumerated the exact constitutional conditions for any court-authorized wiretapping.

Then along came the Omnibus Crime Control and Safe Streets Act of 1968. Section 2511, Title III declared:

> Nothing contained in this statute or in Section 605 of the Communications Act of 1934 . . . shall limit the constitutional powers of the President to take such measures as he deems necessary to protect the Nation against actual or potential attack or other hostile acts. . . . Nor shall anything in this chapter be deemed to limit the Constitutional powers of the President to take such measures as he deems necessary to protect the United States against the overthrow of the government by force or other unlawful means, or against any other clear and present danger to the oral communications intercepted by authority of the President in the exercise of the foregoing powers may be received in evidence . . . only where such interception was reasonable, and shall not otherwise be disclosed except as is necessary to implement that power.

This section seemed to indicate that in cases of "national security" the President was free to bug at will. It did not actually state that no warrant was necessary, but the Nixon Administration apparently interpreted it that way, for Nixon and Attorney General Mitchell—an avid proponent of wiretapping and bugging—acted as if getting a court order was simply too tedious. Besides, a court

order requires that the specific reason for having the surveillance—including the citing of probable cause—be included
with the warrant. And that was a stumbling block for an administration that didn't like to supply answers to what it deemed unnecessary and unreasonable questions. Its position in the matter,
according to Mitchell, was that "the President, acting through the
Attorney General, may constitutionally authorize the use of electronic surveillance in cases where it was determined, that in order
to preserve the national security, the use of such surveillance is
reasonable."

Judge George Edward of the Sixth Circuit Court of Appeals,
hearing a case that revolved around this contention of the "inherent power" of the President, differed radically with Mitchell's
cool assertion of unchecked presidential surveillance. In conclud-
ing his decision, Judge Edward said, "The government has not
pointed to, and we do not find, one written phrase in the Constitution, in the statutory law, or in the case law of the United States,
which exempts the President, Attorney General or Federal law
enforcement from the restrictions of the Fourth Amendment. . . .
The United States Constitution was adopted to provide a check
upon sovereign power. . . . It is strange, indeed, that in this case,
the traditional power of sovereigns like King George III should be
invoked on behalf of an American President to defeat one of the
fundamental freedoms for which the founders of this country
overthrew King George's reign."

And finally, the Supreme Court capped the whole can of worms
when on June 20, 1972, the Court declared that the federal practice
of wiretapping without court order was patently unconstitutional.
The unanimous 8-0 decision must have felt like a sharp slap across
the jowls of the Justice Department, since four of the Eight Old
Men were Nixon appointees.

The opinion was written by Lewis F. Powell, Jr. It may have
been a mere coincidence that Powell was appointed to the high
court following a newspaper article in which he strongly sup-

ported the power of the president to wiretap without court order in cases involving national security. And then again it may not have been a coincidence.

In any case, Powell's opinion noted instead that "the Fourth Amendment freedoms [against "unreasonable searches and seizures"] cannot properly be guaranteed if domestic surveillance may be conducted solely within the discretion of the executive branch.

"History abundantly documents the tendency of government . . . to view with suspicion those who most fervently dispute its policies. The price of lawful public dissent must not be a dread of subjection to an unchecked surveillance power. Nor must the fear of unauthorized official eavesdropping deter vigorous citizen dissent and discussion of Government action in private conversation."

An important result of this decision is that any defendant in a federal prosecution now has the right to peruse complete transcripts of any conversations overheard by the government on a warrantless national-security tap or bug, in order to insure that none of the illegally obtained information is used in the prosecution.

Attorney General Kleindienst, who was generally in favor of warrantless surveillances, vowed to terminate immediately "all electronic surveillance in cases involving security that conflict with the court's opinion." Subsequent surveillance he promised, would be undertaken "only under procedures that comply" with the Court's decision.

Incidentally, the newly appointed Attorney General had presented his credentials to the Court as the government's chief legal officer only minutes before the decision was read. He did not wait around to hear it.

Not too surprisingly, ten days later a Justice Department official told Congress that wiretapping of domestic radicals was continuing despite the Supreme Court's decision and Kleindienst's promises. The Justice Department official did say, however, that the surveillance had been markedly reduced and that "most

—practically all—are foreign intelligence wiretaps.'' The Court's decision had specifically excepted foreign-intelligence gathering from consideration, ruling only on warrantless surveillance in domestic cases.

Former Attorney General Ramsey Clark, speaking on the same subject before the Senate Judiciary Committee hearing, branded wiretapping "absurd and outrageous" and urged that it be completely banned, even in cases involving foreign governments. "Even foreigners have rights," he wryly observed. His testimony pointed out that, in his opinion, the Supreme Court decision would have little effect. He noted that of the eight hundred requests for wiretaps in 1971, none were refused. Clark concluded that it "will always be possible for the executive branch to obtain warrants."

Legal furor and doubletalk aside, one wonders just how many wiretaps and bugs are really in existence and just how effective they really are, and if it is possible to get any straight answers on the subject. For the answers which have been given are obscured by ambiguities, contradictions, and deceit.

The late J. Edgar Hoover noted in January 1972 that the conviction rate of gangsters was on the rise and attributed this to evidence gleaned from electronic surveillance devices. "These devices," Hoover reported, "have been increasingly valuable in penetrating the complex, tightly knit conspiracies involving intricate security precautions, and most of the 1,200 arrests under the Organized Crime Control Act were made possible by them." He cited the rise from 468 convictions in 1970 to more than 650 in 1971 and again insisted that "much of the credit for this gain should go to court approved electronic surveillance devices provided for in recent legislation."

According to a number of suppliers, the government is still a very large purchaser of electronic surveillance equipment, and since they say most uses are for foreign intelligence, it is not surprising that one dealer in the Washington, D.C., area said most of his customers were what he described as "foreigners." Retaliation?

The foreign embassies and United Nations delegations have good reason to suspect the United States of using electronic equipment to surreptitiously glean information from their confidential conversations or communications. At one time or another, the United States has allegedly bugged the embassies of India, the Dominican Republic, Pakistan, Cambodia, Burma, and Egypt, to name a few.

(The USSR, on the other hand, bugs its own embassy, as well as the offices of the Soviet Mission to the United Nations. The surveillance equipment, it has been said, is so multitudinous and sensitive that a fly would barely have time to say a prayer before its tiny little footsteps were noted and pinpointed by equipment, and the fly unceremoniously executed.)

Despite the demand for their equipment, a number of suppliers and distributors of surveillance equipment, among them the previously mentioned Continental Telephone Supply, have gone out of business. They give as reasons for their demise the increasing restrictions on their trade. One former manufacturer—still active in other areas of law enforcement equipment—told us that the government cracked down strongly on any advertising or even manufacturing of any surveillance equipment. When his company began to market a device that could decipher the telephone number of a touch-tone telephone by electronically transmitting the sound into graphics, he got a letter from the Attorney General requesting a list of every customer that had bought one.

Yet, in the next breath, he admitted that "the law hasn't done much good in most areas. I don't think there's really been much of a change in wiretapping or bugging operations because of the Supreme Court or Government harassment [of private eavesdroppers]. If a private party still wants a transmitter in an olive or a microphone in a lamp, he can get it without much of a problem. All it takes is some green stuff thrown in the right direction. For that reason, they'll [equipment manufacturers] never really all go out of business or be driven out of business. Where there's a demand there will always be someone to supply."

According to experts—depending on who you listen to —electronic surveillance is (a) on the decline or (b) on the rise. Pick one. Let's look at some of the reams of statistics they cite.

In 1969, seven states (New Jersey, New York, Arizona, Colorado, Florida, Georgia, and Maryland) accounted for 304 wiretap requests, of which only 2 were denied. Of these, 192 were extended beyond 30 days. Some were in operation for as long as 220 days. Thirteen thousand people were overheard. Of the 414 wiretaps further permitted by state courts, New Jersey accounted for 132 and New York for 215, fully 80 percent of the total. 200,000 conversations involving more than 30,000 people were overheard.

In 1970, New Jersey's court-approved taps listened in on over 19,000 persons. Only New York had more taps in operation, 254 compared to New Jersey's 187. The taps intercepted almost 400,000 conversations between 25,000 persons. New Jersey's massive campaign that year resulted in exactly two convictions . . . for gambling.

Federal wiretappers accounted for another 285 orders issued by federal judges. Of this number, only 47 were in New York and 37 in New Jersey. The remainder were concentrated in cities where the Federal Strike Force against organized crime was most active.

New York, in the business since 1895, has an added distinction of late. The state permits surveillance for a period of up to 30 days with a possible extension of another 30 days, with a possible extension of still another 30 days under special circumstances. Yet, according to the May 5, 1971, *New York Times*, State Supreme Court Justice John P. Cohalan, Jr., allowed two wiretaps to remain in operation far in excess of the statutes, one for 300 days, and the other for 291 days. Other New York counties allowed phones to be tapped in excess of 100 days. The report which released these figures, compiled by the administrative office of the U.S. courts, noted that wiretapping for longer than 20 days was rare anywhere outside of New York.

None of the above wiretaps include any of the devices used

without court authority by the federal government in national security cases. The far-from-complete information available tends to suggest that the number is fewer than those used in criminal cases, but they are left in operation far longer—Senator Edward Kennedy estimated up to ten times as long.

Professor Herman Schwartz of the State University of New York at Buffalo, quoting similar statistics for 1969 and 1970, confronted the question of costs versus effectiveness of electronic surveillance in his paper "Summary of the Findings on the Amount, Benefits, and Costs of Official Electronic Surveillance." Issued by the American Civil Liberties Union in 1972, the paper argues that, contrary to Hoover's glowing testimonial, governmental use of surveillance equipment actually results in very few convictions; that the costs of the eavesdropping have been grossly understated, even though federal and state officials pegged $3 million as the cost for 1970; and the social costs, nowhere taken into consideration, outweigh the dubious benefits anyway. Mr. Schwartz noted that federal eavesdropping in 1970 had produced 48 convictions and 613 arrests out of 10,260 people and 147,780 conversations overheard. Only 21 of these cases were not involved with gambling or drugs, and none of these resulted in convictions. In conclusion he stated, "It would, of course, be foolish to contend that electronic surveillance is of no value, but the privacy of at least tens of thousands of people has been invaded and many millions of dollars are being spent at a time when social services, which might help to get at the roots of the forces that breed crime, are being starved."

Recent evidence suggest that federal agencies are cutting down on court-authorized wiretapping, but that states (notably New York and New Jersey) are making up the loss. From 1970 to 1972, wiretapping by state law enforcement officials rose 43 percent. Of the 855 orders for wiretaps approved by judges in 1972, 294, or 45 percent of the state orders took place in the New York metropolitan area and 235, or 36 percent, took place in New Jersey. This leaves only 19 percent for the rest of the country.

Senator John L. McClellan disclosed the figures on wiretapping in a Senate speech. "These are indeed impressive figures," the Senator said, when he revealed that in the two and one-half years' experience of the Omnibus Crime Control Act of 1968, a total of 2,742 wiretapping orders approved by judges produced 5,956 arrests and 2,495 convictions.

Each of the authorized interceptions in 1972, the senator droned on, involved agents' overhearing about 600 calls, on the average, over a period of about two weeks. Compared to a national figure of 159 billion calls, the surveillance was small, "almost too small to calculate—less than .0000039 percent.

"The privacy of the average citizen, in short, is not threatened by court-ordered surveillance," he concluded.

It's wonderful what you can do with statistics, isn't it? Thirty nine ten-millionths of a percent is so very small. But consider this. During the year 39,600 calls were overheard (an average of 600 calls in a two week period) and of these 50 percent were *judged by agents* (not the courts) to be incriminating. That leaves 19,800 overheard "private" conversations not even judged incriminating by the agents themselves. And most of these almost-twenty-thousand calls were concentrated in the New Jersey and New York metropolitan areas. They don't make all the 159 billion calls that is the national figure. So the .0000039 percent figure is a little ridiculous, isn't it?

But it is also ridiculous for us to start looking under the bed for hidden microphones or to dust the telephone for suspicious finger-prints. The chances are slim that you—average American good citizen—must constantly worry each time you pick up the tele-phone that someone, somewhere is really listening in via a court-approved tap.

Of course, there's always the illegal taps to worry about.

And you can worry about whether the figures given out about the legal wiretaps are really believable. After all, they are given out by the government, aren't they?

The record of the Nixon administration, even without

consideration of the most flagrant case—Watergate—was not overly credible, especially in regards to electronic spying statistics. Consider the following three events, all occurring within a seven-month span.

In September 1970 the Solicitor General reported a total of thirty-six warrantless telephone taps in effect. A March 1971 report to the Senate Administrative Practices Subcommittee from Assistant Attorney General Robert Mardian reported ninety-six taps, almost triple the figure cited only six months before. Finally, one month later, President Nixon himself made everything perfectly clear. "Now in the two years that we have been in office, now get this number, the total number of taps for national security purposes by the FBI, and I know because I look not at the information but at the decisions that are made—the total number of taps is less, has been less, than fifty a year."

Thus, despite the constantly shifting figures cited by government spokesmen whenever the subject arises, a number of factors seriously discredit any figure quoted by anyone. No one really knows, outside of the federal bureaucracy, just how many taps and/or bugs are operated illegally year in and year out. An overlooked area for issue-starved investigators is the Justice Department's concurrent reluctance to prosecute anyone for wiretapping. In the ten-year period 1952-1961, before any of the legal loopholes had been closed, the Department initiated only fourteen cases of wiretap violations. All of the cases concerned private individuals, despite widespread and adequately publicized abuse of wiretapping privileges by federal agencies, state and local law-enforcement officials, the FBI, and the armed forces. One is even forced to overlook the many cases of private infractions of the law which went unpunished, and apparently, deliberately unnoticed.

It is true that state and local law-enforcement officials have grown noticeably cautious in the face of recent Supreme Court decisions, but there is little evidence that private investigators have inherited their caution.

"Super Cop" David Greenburg of the New York Police Department, summed it up this way: "To my knowledge, there is no longer any wiretapping or bugging done by the police without court approval. Before the recent laws were enacted, it was pretty widespread and mostly illegal. Now a cop would have to be stupid—everybody is playing their hand real close. No one would dare do anything without a court order."

But, when asked about the private detectives and other individuals not subject to the same public scrutiny as police officials, Mr. Greenburg admitted, "Big and small, if they've got the money, they'll get it (electronic surveillance equipment) no matter how many laws are passed."

According to many other knowledgeable sources, if a local law-enforcement official wishes to initiate a wiretap with the proper court approval, dealing with the telephone company is easier than getting a dial tone. Most of the telephone companies around the country will even supply the necessary equipment to the grateful police. Besides the wholehearted cooperation of the telephone network, most of which was forthcoming long before any question of legality was involved, the telephone company has taken part in its own privacy-invading surveillance. As Bernie Spindel, one of the best-known surveillance experts and author of *The Ominous Ear*, once said, "when a citizen does it, it's wiretapping; for the FBI, it's monitoring; the telephone company calls it observing."

This observance is rather wide-eyed too. In 1965, the American Telephone and Telegraph Company and its subsidiaries monitored a total of 39.5 million calls. They employed 2,500 fulltime "observers," with thousands more on a "when needed" basis, at a total cost of $19 million. They also admitted monitoring 500,000 telephones in federal offices throughout the country. Company spokesmen reiterated again and again that all this was merely to check on their operators to insure "proper and polite service for the millions of our customers." Few civil libertarians really felt that this lame excuse boasted much validity, since many talkative employees later admitted that rarely had they gotten off the line after conversations had begun, as spokesmen had insisted. Under pressure from Senator Long's subcommittee, telephone-company monitoring was officially ended on June 1, 1966.

However, if our very random sample of one telephone company employee is any indication, seven years after having been legislated out of existence, monitoring still goes on. Our method of obtaining this information was neither scientific nor complex. We simply placed a number of collect long-distance calls, during which a conversation was struck up with various operators, usually very briefly, while the proper switching was accomplished. None of the calls was accepted, but finally, our patience was rewarded—a friendly and talkative operator. The conversation, reconstructed in its entirety and as accurately as possible from hastily scribbled notes, went something like this:

After a sigh, indicating the operator was tired, we asked, "Sure must be a rough job, sitting and facing a switchboard all day, huh?"

"Boy, you know it. It's really a drag. I don't think I'll make it through the summer."

"Yeah, I know what you mean. My wife used to work for the phone company. Couldn't handle it. Two months and she was out. Best thing that ever happened."

"Believe me," the operator said in a sympathetic tone of voice, "I know how she felt."

"You know what finally got to her?"

"What?"

"Those monitors. Always checking on how she was doing. She could never tell if they were patching into her line. It was a hassle every time I talked to her on the phone. She got so paranoid. She still hates to use the phone. She knows that any call could be monitored by everybody and their brother."

"Boy, you know it!" the operator said. "My boyfriend just won't call me any more and I won't call him. I have to wait till I get out of this place."

"You know that's kind of surprising. I mean, my wife worked

for the Telephone Company eight years ago when the monitoring was secretive and no one really knew what was happening. I thought they stopped it around sixty-six, though.''

''Hell, no,'' said the operator. ''They've got some [administrators and supervisors] upstairs in another room that just patch in whenever they want. And the [executive] offices uptown can always listen in whenever they want to.''

''Aren't you afraid they're listening in on this call?''

''Nah. If they were, someone would have been down here five minutes ago. We're not allowed to say a heck of a lot more than 'Number, pleeze,' to customers.''

And that was the end of the conversation.

Was it true? Or was she imagining things? Had an insubstantial rumor become—to her—a reality? We tended to believe that perhaps she was mistaken, because if you can't believe the telephone company, who can you believe?

But it was curious.

Chapter Two:

The State of
the Bug

"Respect for privacy is certainly not innate among primates . . . only the gorilla and the orangutan seem deficient in the urge to snoop; these dignified and noble beasts shrink equally from exposing themselves to publicity and from intruding upon the privacy of others. Both are near extinction."—Joseph W. Bishop, the New York Times *magazine*

There is nothing wrong with being curious, of course. Without our curiosity, we'd probably still be swinging through the trees, also near extinction like the orangutan and the gorilla. But a lack of curiosity will never make man extinct. In fact, if curiosity were one of the requirements for eternal life—which it probably is —man would never die.

But like that famous cat, too much curiosity might kill us. For there is a frightening difference between natural curiosity—or human nosiness—on the one hand, and the ominous assaults on privacy by the use of increasingly sophisticated electronic and chemical equipment, on the other.

It seems our curiosity has run away with us. And we now find ourselves in an awkward state of electronic overkill. To enhance

26

the effectiveness and efficiency of our knowledge-gathering capabilities, to appease our insatiable curiosity, we have developed highly effective substitutes for our ears, eyes, and minds, equipment which is so effective that the mere use of it automatically invades somebody's privacy, as we Americans have always defined the word.

The devices are wireless, effortless, and practically detection-proof, as we have said, they require almost no electronic skill to operate and come already disguised—in some cases—so we don't have to strain ourselves in a search for hiding places. And small —they can fit into cufflinks, tieclasps, desk calendars, fountain pens, and even—again—that infamous martini olive.

Their versatility is also endless. They can be slid under doors, dropped out of windows, nailed into walls, put into tooth cavities, and—in fact—adapted to just about any place you can think of.

Most of the following equipment came from a catalogue put out by Sirchie Fingerprint Laboratories of Maryland, 5518 Western Avenue, Chevy Chase, Maryland 20015. The catalogue numbers and prices—when they appear—are Sirchie's. ("Search with Sirchie—Products for Results" and "Be Certain with Sirchie!" are their catalogue mottos.) None of this equipment is legally available to the general public.

The Famous Martini-Olive Microphone: Mentioned in the 1966 Senate hearings on bugging devices, this little jewel is not as effective as it looks. Its range is only about fifty feet and it is fairly expensive, about $200.00. The microphone is situated at the left end of the olive where the hole normally is. The toothpick conceals the aerial. A recorder and receiver would have to be located in a nearby room in order to pick up the olive's transmission. It is not recommended for professionals, because it is basically a gimmick.

Wristwatch Microphone: For those intimate little moments, the mike is concealed in the watch-case. The manufacturers say it is excellent for use with transmitters or tape recorders secreted on the

1. Martini-olive microphone
2. Cuff-link microphone
3. Tie-clip microphone
4. Button-hole microphone
5. Fountain-pen microphone
6. Wrist-watch microphone
7. Tie-pin microphone

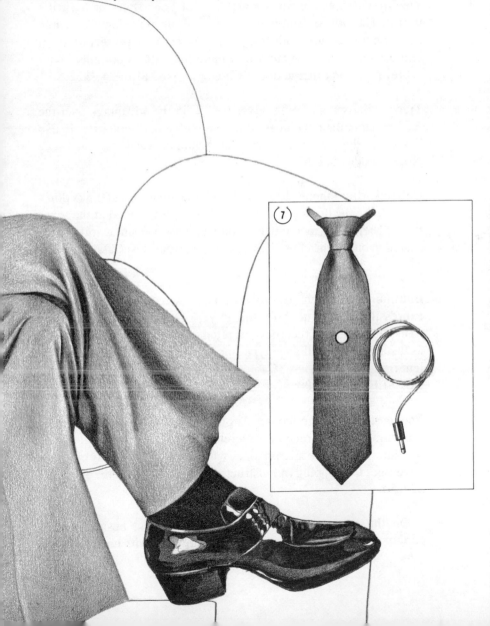

body. The sensitivity is said to be good even when covered by clothing. It comes with a cable and plug. Catalogue No. SLE029. Only $33.00.

Tieclip Microphone: So what if it's not your style; at least it's useful. The clip contains a sensitive, medium-impedance dynamic microphone for use with body transmitters or tape recorders. It reduces clothing noises to a minimum and comes complete with cable, plug, and instructions. Catalogue No. SLE021. $22.50

Tiepin Microphone: What gives the tiepin the advantage over the tieclip is that the pin comes complete with a dark-color tie. It also has a very sensitive mike, cable, plug, and instructions. Catalogue No. SLE024. $31.50.

Cufflink Microphone: The only problem is that the cufflinks don't go with the tieclip or pin, but then both aren't needed at the same time. There is a medium impedance, very sensitive mike concealed in one of the clips. Cable, plug, instructions. Catalogue No. SLE022. $34.50

Buttonhole Microphone: Now we know what they mean by that expression "to buttonhole the guy." This mike is ideal with transmitters or tape recorders secreted on the body. It may be used as a standard surveillance type microphone, also. There is excellent frequency response. Cable, plug, and instructions. Catalogue No. SLE023. $27.00.

Fountain-Pen Microphone: Another which is excellent with transmitters or tape recorders secreted on the body. Very sensitive, medium-impedance microphone, which is not affected by clothing coverage. Cable, plug (no instructions?). Catalogue No. SLE025. $22.50

On the receiving end of these microphones, beside the recorders, there are fantastic computers (the ones with no heart) with the capacity to store overwhelming amounts of overheard conversations—plus other personal and public information —which can be retrieved in seconds, if need be.

And if it's true that a picture is worth a thousand words, there're some pretty good cameras available, such as the one that can photograph from thousands of miles above the earth, producing photos so detailed that one can count the number of soldiers and missiles at an enemy military site, or the number of people walking down a city street, or the number of hippies in a commune.

There are those cameras that can see through walls (The solid-wall camera works on the same principal as the new medical devices which allow doctors to photograph the brain and other organs in layers. In other words, the photo would be more of a "ghost image" than an actual portrait.), photograph you in the darkest night, and even take pictures of your "heat-signature" after you have left the room.

There is literally no place to hide, if all such equipment is utilized.

O.K., we have all this equipment, but do we have to use it? Do we have to store all that information we can get our hands on, just because there's a place to store it? Do we have to photograph every square inch of the earth, keeping track of everybody and everything, just because we can? Do we have to use the supersensitive microphones and the undetectable telephone bugs and the closed-circuit television cameras?

Probably. Because it is just another extension of man's curiosity. Can you imagine our not doing it?

If someone is curious enough to want to overhear a neighbor's family arguments, then wouldn't it be natural for that someone to get something with which to hear better? In TV's hit *All In The Family*, Archie Bunker was listening to his daughter and son-in-law fight by holding an empty drinking glass to the wall and pressing his ear against the closed end. The glass picked up and amplified the vibrations of the voices and Archie could hear better. Now, if Archie had had an obstruction-contact microphone outfit, he could have heard Meathead's mustache wiggle. All he would have had to do was to screw a small spike into the wall, attach it to an amplifier, sit back, and listen. The complete kit containing one stickle-back saw for drilling holes, one obstruction-contact mike, one spike adapter, one long spike, threaded, one short spike, threaded, and complete instructions, would have set him back only $33.50. The outfit is advertised "to facilitate those hard-to-get-to conversations. This . . . will help you listen through doors, walls, and windows."

Today, the nosy father-in-law or the neighborhood gossip has been replaced by these ears which are far more sensitive, more readily replayable, and much more terrifying in their scope. There have been other replacements, of course, and each grows more threatening as the range of the surveillance is increased.

The scout, who probably got his start in the caveman days by sneaking over the hill and listening to the campfire battle-talk or counting the enemy horses, has now been replaced by that orbiting photo-and-electronic-eavesdropping satellite. And the advisors of government—the wise sages of old—are the cold sterile computers of today.

The company spy no longer has to worm his way into the good graces of the dissident workers, so he can report back on the labor negotiations. He has been replaced by the tiny "harmonica bug," which uses the telephone as a permanent source of power. Its installation—a matter of minutes for a professional—is a snap to use, and once installed will pick up everything said within fifty feet of the cradled receiver.

In the CIA, a similar device is called an "infinity microphone" and is reputedly getting a lot of use from that agency. The infinity mike and the harmonica bug have the great advantage of being undetectable by an antibug detector.

A few years back, the bug sold for about four hundred dollars, but now a similar device, under various names, is sold for only a little over two hundred dollars. So not even inflation has pushed the prices up in this field, and you certainly don't have to be rich in order to own some excellent electronic-surveillance equipment. The most-effective, highest-quality bugging job would cost no more than a few thousand dollars. The most expensive part of the set-up is the tape recorder, and depending on the quality of the fidelity required, the recorder can run up to four thousand dollars, or as little as thirty dollars.

In fact, it's so easy and inexpensive to indulge in electronic spying that ever-increasing numbers of private citizens—not to mention private detectives and law-enforcement officers—have been bitten by the bug. They have purchased microphones that "facilitate listening through doors, walls, and windows." They have found "an ideal microphone for use in through wall appliances, in hotel and motel rooms" that is "more sensitive to sound than the human ear."

There is no place you can really be sure of any more. The desk calendar in the boss's office might be recording your offhand "private" remarks. There could be a miniature microphone hidden almost anywhere in your own office, in your motel or hotel room, or in the painting your competitor sent you as a Christmas present.

Desk Pen Microphone: This ballpoint pen and base holder is for the economy-minded. If you never record anything of any importance, the pen still works, so your money is not completely lost. The microphone boasts medium impedance, with excellent sensitivity, and works well with standard commercial recorders. It's a "good choice for interrogations, etc." Comes with cable, plug, and instructions. $21.00. Catalogue No. SLE026. (This equipment and all the others following came from the Sirchie catalogue unless otherwise indicated.)

Desk-Calendar Microphone: The date may not be 1984 on the pages of this calendar, but the feeling is the same as if it were. The

1. **Automatic-picture surveillance transmitter**
2. **Postage-stamp microphone**
3. **Master portable intelligence recording kit**
4. **Desk calendar microphone**
5. **Sub-miniature surveillance microphone**
6. **Desk pen microphone**
7. **Suction-cup microphone**
8. **Rigid tube microphone**
9. **Miniature tube microphone**

microphone is concealed in the base, and has a medium impedance, dynamic mike which works effectively with standard commercial recorders or transmitters. Cable, plug, instructions. Catalogue No. SLE027. $27.50

Rigid-Tube Microphone: An ideal mike to use through wall appliances. The wall outlet box is removed to permit insertion of the tube against the outer wall. Excellent reproduction. Has medium impedance, dynamic microphone with tube, cable, plug, instructions. Catalogue No. SLE015. $16.00.

Miniature-Tube Microphone: All you need is a small nail hole; that's enough clearance for the pick-up tube. For use in windows, doors and wall appliances. Very sensitive. Cable, plug, instructions. Catalogue No. SLE016. $19.50.

Suction-Cup Microphone: An improved method of listening through doors, windows, and walls of single thickness. A medium-impedance, 1,000-ohm supersensitive microphone is embedded in a suction cup. Simply press the cup to a wall, and plug into amplifier, tape recorder, or transmitter. Excellent results have been achieved with this unit in virtually inaccessible places. Catalogue No. SLE017. $22.00.

Postage-Stamp Microphone: It doesn't look like a postage stamp, but it could hide behind one. It is "ideal for concealment in jail cells, interrogation rooms, motel and hotel rooms, etc. More sensitive to sound than the human ear." Cable, plug, and instructions. Catalogue No. SLE018. $17.50.

Sub-miniature Surveillance Microphone: Small enough to fit into the cavity of a tooth. An extremely miniature (5/16" x 5/16" x 1/8") supersensitive mike, excellent for use in rooms, offices, etc. "Easy to hide." Medium impedance, with cable and plug. Catalogue No. SLE019. $26.50.

Master Portable Intelligence Recording Kit: Watch out for the guy in your "recording studio" whom you think you have the jump on. His attaché-case may be concealing a master intelligence-gathering-and-recording kit for the professional. Some of the attaché-case kits contain the microphone right in the handle. This one doesn't, but it does "enable the operator to meet nearly any eventuality involved in surveillance work." Consists of the following:

Intelligence Tape Recorder (battery of 117.VAC)
High-Gain Recorder Preamplifier
Telephone Robot Sentry
Telephone-Line Tracer
Distant-Line Microphone Preamplifier
Telephone-Line Test Lamps (5)
Electronic Voice-Actuator
Telephone Lineman's Test Set
Clamp-On Telephone Coil
Pocket Surveillance Amplifier
Subminiature Surveillance Microphones (2)
Postage-Stamp Microphone
Miniature-Tube Microphone
Rigid-Tube Microphone
Suction-Cup Microphone
Obstruction-Contact Microphone Outfit
Headphones

Various patch cords, recorder adapters, batteries, installation tools, 100-foot microphone wire, instructions. Catalogue No. SLEO34.

Automatic Picture Surveillance Transmitter: FM, crystal-controlled. "An unusual and unique method of concealing a transmitter in a room without lengthy preparations. The transmitter is concealed in the false rear of the picture frame." The frame size is 12×16 inches and has several different scenes which may be readily changed to harmonize with the room décor. Battery life is 240 hours. Automatic on/off switching is accomplished with a remote-control transmitter and receiver. "This method eliminates conventional detection by permitting the investigator to discontinue transmission indiscriminately." Comes with batteries, antennas, microphones, remote transmitters, receivers and instructions. Catalogue No. SLE045. $460.00.

There are other, more exotic, and less readily obtainable items, primarily used for long-distance monitoring. The shotgun microphone, for instance, can be aimed like a gun and has a range of 3,500 feet. It can pick up sound right through a window. The only drawback of the shotgun mike is that it is cumbersome to handle and a bother to record from.

There is also the "Doppler Radar Microphone" which can be disguised as an automobile spotlight. It operates on radar waves and can be bounced off your windowpane, picking up minute vibrations as you hold a private conversation inside. Hooked up to the car radio, the driver hears what you say.

The laser-beam microphone works on the same principle, except that it uses a mirrored modulator from which to bounce the laser beam back to the origin. The beam returns changed only slightly by voice waves. Even from miles away, a photo-amplifier then goes to work to reproduce your words for an interested audience. You've got to admire that kind of electronic technology, don't you?

But the average citizen would be hard-pressed to latch onto a "Doppler Radar" microphone, and even most law-enforcement officers lack the means of getting one. However, you needn't lose any sleep over that; there's plenty of more readily available equipment to worry about, even though it's illegal to make it general knowledge.

Until July 30, 1973, this surveillance equipment *was* advertised and openly displayed with descriptive phrases vividly outlining their exact use. ("For those hard-to-get-to conversations.") Now, according to U.S. Code 18, Section 2512, electronic companies can no longer advertise or seek free exposure in books or magazine articles. Now they can only send their catalogues as a contract solicitation to law enforcement agencies that qualify under the law—primarily city, county, state, federal, and military that are entirely tax-supported and that have the power to arrest or are engaged in that ever-popular government pastime, National Security.

So the window-shopping days for the innocent but curious bystander belong to the past. However, if the Fargo spokesman quoted above is to be believed, window-shopping is the only aspect of surveillance equipment that is missing. If someone wants the equipment badly enough, it can be had.

So you can see how unsuspectingly you can be bugged. Anyone can be bugged. Even the President's brother. (Now there's a man who could literally use the term "Big Brother is watching.")

When it came out during the Watergate hearings—along with all the other government wiretapping escapades—that there had been a wiretap on Donald Nixon's telephone for over a year, many people were appalled. The President's own brother! The wiretap, later acknowledged by the President, was said to have been performed in order to save a high government official from embarrassment. But shouldn't that high government official have felt that, brother or no, Donald was entitled to the privacy or lack of privacy of his own choosing? Or should one assume that if one is a member of the royal family, one automatically forfeits one's civil rights, the same as if one were a prisoner?

But even a prisoner has some rights. And one of those rights is that he is *not* to be bugged.

The town of Wilton, Connecticut, found that out when the Civil Liberties Union warned them that their new Fairfield County Jail could not legally have microphones and television surveillance equipment incorporated into the individual cells.

The reason given for the incorporation of the surveillance

equipment according to Laurence I. Graham, Wilton's First Selectman, was for the prisoner's own good—primarily to avoid suicides.

The Civil Liberties Union recognized that law-enforcement members have serious problems with prison suicides and injuries among intoxicated detainees, but William Olds, director of the local Civil Liberties Union, stated that "it is disturbing that a town such as Wilton should assume that electronic bugging does not pose a substantial threat to liberty. Such bugging assumes that a government is unable to assure its citizens' personal security without invading their privacy." He went on to say that "you cannot invade a person's privacy without specific court permission," and that a violation of the federal law carries a fine of not more than $10,000 or imprisonment for not more than five years.

After hearing of the Civil Liberties Union's efforts to stop the future surveillance of their prisoners, the First Selectman said that there was plenty of time to reconsider the plans. Perhaps the thought of the whole town council being imprisoned for a time within those all-seeing, all-hearing walls was enough for a reconsideration.

But in any case, it's a minor point, isn't it? How many of us will ever be in the Wilton, Connecticut, jail? And if we were, wouldn't we deserve a little privacy-invasion?

It may be a small matter on a national scale, but it is privacy-invasion nonetheless; a little chip here and a little chip there, and the whole Fourth Amendment falls down around our collective ears. We are in less danger from one national Big Brother than from a series of little brothers—the little brothers that are the computerized credit records; the wide use of government and commercial surveys: the possibilities that every one of our phones could be bugged, that cable TV could be turned into an all-seeing eye invading our livingrooms or bedrooms, that all the super-sophisticated electronic equipment that is available could effectively be used to deprive every one of us of any shred of privacy. And the possibility that one night—innocent though we might be—we are booked into a clean, well-lighted jail cell where our every movement, mutter of despair, or hostile threat is watched by some never-sleeping eye.

One thing that allows the widespread use of surveillance equipment, whether by government or by private parties, is public apathy. It's certainly not because attention is never focused on the issue. In 1966, a Senate subcommittee under the chairmanship of Senator Edward V. Long received much publicity for their investigation into Administrative Practice and Procedure. The main objectives of the hearings were "to try to ascertain who the big users of snooping gear are and what justification, if any, can be found for such use."

The conclusion that Senator Long reached was that "privacy is necessary to the development of a free and independent people. To preserve this privacy, our national lethargy and lack of knowledge must be countered. . . . People must be made to realize that, little by little, they are losing their right to privacy. Once they become aware of this, I think they will shake off their apathy and demand action. Then, and only then, will we get strong legislation to protect a reasonable amount of our right to be left alone."

But three years later, the Senate found it necessary to authorize still another investigation to ascertain who the big users of snooping gear were, and what legislation would either halt or better control it.

Senator Sam Ervin, Jr., who chaired the later hearings, remarked during one of these hearings that "one device in particular deserves particular attention. Wiretapping, that sneaky business that has become a plaything in America—especially in the government—during the past few years, has become a term on the tongue of every American. . . . I have become convinced that its rampant use is not consonant with a free society."

Well, consonant or not, its use is still rampant.

During still another Senate investigation that touched on the use of snooping gear—this time the Watergate Committee—Chairman Sam Ervin was shown how "that sneaky business" was actually performed. James W. McCord, Jr., a witness at the hearings and one of the nation's better-known wiretappers, uncovered a telephone receiver and described how the tap—consisting of a transmitter, two wires, and a small antenna—was concealed inside the telephone itself. According to McCord, the two wires could be "interconnected in series with the wiring within the phone," and drawing on the telephone's power, would continue to operate for several months.

The device McCord demonstrated, not only to Chairman Sam but to a nationwide audience, was relatively unsophisticated and would probably have cost no more than fifty dollars. Although effective and—unless actually searched for, which it was —undetectable, it is surprising that the government would use a device so unsophisticated now that they've been in the wiretapping business for such a long time. They have been using, along with lots of others, much better bugs.

"Almost everybody in the business today uses the telephone as an all purpose bugging unit. It's easily hidden as a bugging device, for the simple reason that nobody suspects it.

"Everybody's bugging everybody. If you hear my voice getting weaker suddenly it probably means your phone's tapped too."

An unidentified source spoke those words in recent news stories. The focus of the stories, of course, was the bugging of the President's phones in the White House, and several other bugging operations—Watergate, the Gainesville Eight, several radical lawyers, newsmen, loyal public servants, various campaign headquarters—some proven, some merely alleged.

The point all these stories share is that each of us has a very vulnerable bugging spot. Our telephones. In a recent survey concerning the standard of living in the world, it was found that there is one telephone for every four persons in the United States. The most in the world. Everybody uses a telephone at some time or another. And unless we happen to be on a known party line, we usually believe our conversations are private. Of course, they might be. But the telephone *is* a bugger's delight.

It is rumored that wiretapping started way back when. Mickey (Cheesebox) Callihan was an electronics wizard from The Bronx, and he supposedly bedeviled the police with a crude little wire-jumping device. Cheesebox was a bookmaker, and he used the device to make free calls.

Today's gadgets are so sophisticated that Cheesebox would probably have gone into a state of rapture over them. One such, called the Blue Box, has the telephone company in an uproar. The box imitates the six basic telephone company wave frequencies—which AT&T innocently published in a technical journal some time ago—and by calling a tollfree "800" area code, the Blue Box holder can keep "dialing" telephone numbers around the world. All free of charge. A lot of the so-called counterculture figures—active in the late sixties—found the box cut down their phone bills quite a bit. Most of them used it "innocently" enough. Only the phone company suffered. But the box could also have been used to intercept a phone call already in progress. Attached to a tape recorder, it was a very effective phonetapping device.

The use of the Blue Box is still apparently widespread, for a Concord, New Hampshire firm—Northeast Electronics Corporation—is mass-producing an "anti-Blue Box" gadget which is selling briskly to telephone companies.

We already mentioned the infinity microphone, which allows you to transform the earpiece of a telephone into a long-distance bug, and its cousin, the harmonica bug, which does the same thing. Here, then, is more optional equipment for telephones from Sirchie:

Telephone Induction Coil: This extremely sensitive miniature telephone induction coil does not need direct contact with a telephone line or terminals. Conversations may be picked up ten inches away from the instrument. "This is of great value near a telephone booth." Operates with transmitters, audio amplifiers, and recorders. Catalogue No. SLE029. $14.50

1. Telephone line tracer
2. Telephone-interception kit
3. Automatic telephone
4. Telephone dialing interpretro
5. Drop-in FM transmitter
6. Super-sensitive contact microphone
7. Telephone induction coil
8. Clamp-on telephone induction coil
9. Self-powered FM telephone transmitter

Clamp-On Telephone Induction Coil: This device clamps around the wire (only one) but does not actually have to touch it. Picks up both sides of a conversation and the number dialed. Excellent reproduction. 600-ohm impedance. Use with transmitters, tape recorders, or surveillance audio amplifiers. Instructions supplied. Catalogue No. SLE028. $37.00.

Telephone-Dialing Interpreter: This instrument works on either standard-dial or touch-tone-dialing signals. It permits conversion into handy numerical read-out for positive identification of phone numbers. It can be either hooked to a tape recorder, or connected directly to a "suspect" line for a read-out as the number is dialed. Solid state, integrated-circuit logic system. Instructions. Catalogue No. SLE069. $890.00.

Self-Powered FM Telephone Transmitter (Parasitic): Powered by the current of the telephone line, it transmits only when the telephone is in use. May easily be installed in the base of any telephone, including the pushbutton multiline type, or anywhere on the line or telephone. Catalogue No. SLE058-59. $160.00.

Drop-In FM Transmitter (Parasitic): A miniature transmitter around a carbon microphone element of a standard phone. "Requires only fifteen seconds to install in the mouthpiece." No batteries required. Catalogue No. SLE060. $190.00.

Supersensitive Contact Mike: The greatest for listening through the walls of a telephone booth, or the walls of an adjoining office. Called the most sensitive contact mike in the world. Can be carried in the pocket until ready to place against the booth or wall. Catalogue No. SLE064. $57.00.

Automatic Telephone-Line Interceptor: "Cannot be detected by the telephone company or conventional defensive equipment." This remarkable unit for telephone surveillance when actuated by the telephone, instantly turns the recorder on, records the number being dialed and both sides of the conversation, and then turns the recorder off when the phone is not in use. A selector knob permits easy connection for each type of installation. Dial reads: Norm. Tone. Pay. Bat. Off. Complete with adapter cords, batteries and instructions. Catalogue No. SLE010. $175.00.

Telephone-Line Tracer: A must when installing telephone-interception devices. Self-contained, with battery life of six hundred hours. Has a fixed-tone generator for tracing telephone wires. May be attached to any line without interference. Injects 600-cycle tone so that the telephone wires and terminals may be traced from the telephone to the main. Comes with clip leads, battery, instructions. Catalogue No. SLE012. $43.90.

Telephone-Interception Kit: This has the whole thing in one bag. It contains:

Pocket Amplifier (Integrated Circuitry)
Telephone-Line Tracer
Telephone Lineman's Test Set
Telephone-Line Test Lamps (5)
Miniature Telephone Induction Coil
Telephone Robot Sentry
Clamp-On Telephone Coil
Set Installation Tools
Various patch cords, recorder adapters, batteries, and instructions. Catalogue No. SLE013. $329.00

You can see, then, that the private phone you are using could very well be hooked into a "party line." There are many more such devices, but we're sure you've got the idea.

There is one more item we might mention, however. It's called a "hook switch bypass." Concealed inside the phone, it can be switched to record either face-to-face conversations or telephone conversations. And it can easily be turned off remotely if the victim is employing counterbugging measures. If, by chance, the eavesdropper wishes to record while these antibugging devices are in use, all he has to do is pipe music through the bug at such a low level that it cannot be heard by the human ear. It throws the sensitive equipment searching for it off completely.

Bugging is by no means an American phenonomen. In fact, Americans were about the only people in the world who were shocked by the recent government-inspired surveillance and bugging. Other countries more or less expect such things. In Paris, a high government official told the French Senate in June 1973 that government wiretapping was none of its business. And that the government would continue to order the tapping of telephones as required.

Parisians had long accepted wiretapping as a necessary evil for reasons of national security, and they gave a Gallic shrug at the activity. However, news reports said that the practices spread from the security area to political espionage, and the government was most concerned about radical leftwing political activities "whose aim is to attack the republic's institutions and to destroy them."

That quote sounds as if it might have come straight out of the Watergate hearings, and gives chilling evidence as to how broad and unsatisfactory such words are when used to explain a loss of civil liberties. In fact, when the d'Estaing administration took over the French government in June 1974, President d'Estaing apparently felt the same way. For in his program to bring "change" to France, he formally decreed an end to widespread wiretapping by government snoopers.

Other countries seem to be waking up, too. In England a commission headed by Sir Kenneth Younger reported to the House of Commons the current dangers to British privacy. A flurry of debates and proposed legislation to deal with illegitimate forms of surveillance, give individuals the right of access to credit-rating information and protect them against harassment by collection agencies, have appeared. There was also discussion about a computer-watchdog committee to watch over not only computerized records but survey research as well.

The United Nations is also trying to get into the picture. Secretary General Waldheim announced that he planned to submit a report on bugging sometime in 1974 to the United Nations Commission on Human Rights. The study, he said, would take up "uses of electronics which may affect the rights of the person and the limits which should be placed on such uses in a democratic society."

If the UN is as effective in doing something about the use of bugging as they are in doing something about the other threats to human rights, then we've still got a lot to worry about. It seems the folks who bug will keep right on bugging, and will be able to say, with Bernard Bates Spindel (once the number-one big-league freelance eavesdropper and wiretapper in the US):

"It all began to give me a special feeling of power to know what everyone in that building was saying and what they were doing. I've never lost that feeling. I have knowledge that no one else in the *world* has about certain individuals."

Chapter Three:

Friends of the Bug

"Like Orwell's pigs, all bodies emit heat, only some bodies emit more heat. Indeed a body—be it human or automobile—can depart from a particular site and leave its signature behind, which can be 'seen' for some time afterwards. An infrared detector or heat sensor can spot it, as the Pentagon revealed when it distributed a photograph showing the heat signature or ghost image of a man who wasn't there."—Howard Simons, Esquire, *May 1966*

Although direct eavesdropping—the bugging of a room or building and telephone taps—appears to be the most insidious and widespread threat to your personal privacy, there are other, almost as frightening, and just as threatening means of finding out all about you. For instance, that camera described above. Imagine that.

Not only can they catch you while you're doing what you're doing, but if they happened to have messed up and missed your rendezvous, they can come later and photograph your heat signature still doing what you were doing. It would make you think twice before cheating on your wife or husband if you knew that minutes after your passion was spent and the other party had left, your suspicious spouse could photograph an empty bedroom and develop quite a divorce case.

And speaking of cheating, it would do you no good to rent a secret hideway under an assumed name, even if you're an expert at losing a tail. Not if your mate has heard of the radio transmitter disguised as a coat button. Once sewn onto your suit jacket, the follower no longer needs to be adept or quick or clever. Now he can stay a discreet distance behind you, completely out of sight, while your traitorous coat gives off those ever-easy-to-follow radio signals. Of course, your spouse need not have been the one to have sewed on the button. If anyone were interested enough to use this device, he could approach the neighborhood dry-cleaning establishment which you patronize, and by showing a few dollars or the shiny silver of a badge, could probably persuade someone in the shop to see the way to a quick button-switch. Would you ever notice? How often do you check to see if all the buttons are exactly alike when your clothes come back from the cleaners?

There are various other items to enhance the ancient art of shadowing. The radio pill described in the introduction could also be fed to you. Since it is smaller than an aspirin tablet, it could easily be hidden in your cherrystone clams. Once it was settled in your stomach, you would be a walking broadcast station for six hours or more.

There is a powder which could be spread in your path—powder which gives off a faint radioactive signal leaving a telltale trail to where your shoes are hiding under a bed—or a conference table.

Any of the various miniature microphones could be adapted to give off a signal and slipped into your pocket, given to you, hidden in a box of matches, cigarettes, or what have you.

And if you think you can fool them all by waiting more than six hours after eating, running out to your car in the middle of the night, stripping nude, and driving away to your secret meeting, you have another think coming.

There are gadgets for cars, too. Gadgets which clamp magnetically to the metal frame and just keep right on beeping away to the guy behind you, saving him a lot of work and worry about losing you in traffic.

There are binoculars (called variously Find-R-Scope, Scan-R-Scope, Ni-Tec, etc.) that allow someone to see in the darkest night and also allow that someone to take pictures of you. But all these items are just embellishments on that oldest of all surveillance methods—one human being following another. The tail.

Ralph Nader had one. Not a very good one, it turned out, but nevertheless a set of real live detectives hired to find out all about him for General Motors. That was back in the early sixties when GM was having quite a big problem with their little car—the rear-engined Corvair.

Nader's book *Unsafe At Any Speed* was making large waves that threatened to swamp the GM car. The company was being sued by various Corvair owners at the time Nader's book came out with his views on the dangers of driving the car. So moves were made by men in high places to put Ralph Nader down. All they had to do, these men reasoned, was to find out exactly what made Nader tick, and use this information against him.

Among the instructions received by the detectives who participated in the surveillance were these:

> The above-mentioned (Ralph Nader) is a free-lance writer and attorney. Recently he published a book, UN-SAFE AT ANY SPEED, highly critical of the automotive industry's interest in safety. Since then our client's client has made some cursory inquiries into Nader to ascertain his expertise, his interests, his background, etc. They have found out relatively little about him. . . .
> Our job is to check his life and current activities to determine "what makes him tick," such as his real interest in safety, his supporters, if any, his politics, his marital status, his friends, his women, his boys, etc. drinking, dope, jobs—in fact, all facets of his life.

During this surveillance of Nader, a private citizen, by a giant corporation, approximately sixty of his friends and relatives were interviewed by the detectives trying to find out about "his women, his boys, etc." They were told that Nader was being considered for an important job with some unnamed—but also important—party.

Nader came out of his investigation "clean," and during a special hearing of a Senate subcommittee (since he was a witness before a subcommittee on automotive safety at the time, GM's surveillance of him came under the subcommittee's scrutiny as harassment of a government witness), General Motors' president, James Roche, apologized. He said he had not known of the surveillance, it had been ordered by other executives in the firm, and it would not happen again.

But it did happen that time. And it probably is still happening to other people by other company's orders. And what would the apology have meant if there had been discovered something less than aboveboard in Nader's background? Would his private misdeeds have discredited his legitimate public concern for automotive safety?

How many of us would have come out from such an investigation as clean as Nader did? Squeaky-clean Americans probably number very few. There is always something. Or at least almost always. And there is a way of finding out if someone wants to badly enough, especially if you attract too much attention to yourself, as Nader did by writing his book.

Or as Louise Mulligan did by not applauding President Nixon's speech in 1972.

Louise Mulligan is the wife of James Mulligan, a Navy captain who was shot down over Vinh on March 20, 1966. For six and a half years, she waited for her husband's return. Then in 1972 Louise, along with wives and families of other men lost or imprisoned in Southeast Asia, was in the audience at the Statler Hotel in New York City when President Nixon addressed the gathering. When the President completed his speech, most of the audience rose and applauded. Louise Mulligan did not. She saw no reason, she later said, to applaud a man who had "continued this terrible war for four more years."

Immediately afterwards, Louise Mulligan noticed a man closely watching her. He was carrying a walkie-talkie and he appeared to be one of the Secret Service men who constantly surround the President. As she left the lobby of the hotel, she overheard the man saying something to the effect of "she is now leaving the hall. . . ."

Anthony Lewis, reporting the incident in the New York *Times*, said that "Mrs. Mulligan told some of the other wives about her experience, saying how ironic she thought it was that we were supposed to be fighting for democracy in South Vietnam and then found things like this happening at home. Two of her friends later saw the man who followed her, and went up and asked who he was. He replied that he was a postal inspector."

What exactly was he doing and why had he made it so obvious? Was it a threat? Or just a clumsy job? Either way it's pretty frightening, and not something we relish happening to us, not anymore than Louise Mulligan did. There are times when you don't feel like applauding the President.

It is more than likely in the eyes of the government that Mrs. Mulligan had done more than sit on her hands. It is doubtful if that in itself would have been enough for the "postal inspector" to watch over her. But it is also doubtful that she had done anything which was enough to have justified the surveillance.

Among other government agents who conduct surveillance on private citizens, besides "postal inspectors," are IRS agents. The IRS has admitted bugging public and private telephones, and even rooms where IRS auditors called businessmen for questioning, on the theory that this might reveal something when the IRS men stepped out of the room.

There is, it is rumored, a certain amount of reading other people's mail by Uncle Sam, too. Representative Durward G. Hall said on January 18, 1971, that he was "personally and very deeply concerned about the fact that Big Uncle is not only watching over us, but on occasion, he is also seizing and reading our mail. And reading our mail before it has been delivered."

Asked to comment on this observation, the then Deputy General Counsel for the Post Office Department, Harvey H. Hannah, asserted that "it has been established that judicial seizures of mail do not violate the Constitutional guarantees of the Fourth Amendment to the Constitution."

So much for the privacy of the mail.

During the Senate subcommittee hearings on Administrative Practices and Procedures, it turned out that besides all the law enforcement agencies and "civilian" agencies—such as the IRS—that were routinely employing electronic snooping gear, big business also used snooping equipment—not necessarily to spy on outsiders, as in the case of GM and Nader, but to spy on their own employees.

Closed-circuit television, dressing rooms with two-way mirrors, bugs, and a gimmick called Service Observing Equipment, are often used. The telephone company, which rented the SOE's to other service businesses that wished to spy on their employees undetected, said the equipment was to insure that the businesses' services were being adequately performed.

In large department stores, closed-circuit TV cameras are used to watch for shoplifters. That's fairly well known. But did you also know that two-way mirrors have been employed in dressing rooms for the same purpose? That is where much of the clothing which is shoplifted is hidden. Thus the use of the mirrors is justified. But still, doesn't it make you feel a little uneasy to think that the mirror you are undressing in front of might be concealing a pair of beady little eyes?

The rub comes—so often—with cases such as those of stores which have a legitimate reason to watch their customers. Shoplifters steal thousands of dollars' worth of merchandise every day, and we—who don't shoplift—end up paying for it. So why not let them use two-way mirrors and closed-circuit television cameras? Why not lose a little privacy to save ourselves some money?

Why complain about service companies using Service Observing Equipment to insure that *we* get better service from *their* employees?

"There is no clear line between freedom and repression. Freedom is a fluid, intangible condition of our society. It thrives at some periods and is beset at others. It is lost not all at a time, but by degrees," says that old country lawyer Sam Ervin.

Let us take another case of the questionable use of modern electronic-surveillance equipment. The New York City Police Department last year announced its intention to set up a van in Times Square with videotape recorders to receive pictures from cameras which were to be hidden in strategic locations around the area. The cameras would work as a deterrent to crime, because of the publicity they would receive, or so it was believed by the proponents of the hidden cameras.

But could it also be, as the New York Civil Liberties Union believes, an attack on privacy? "A disturbing step toward a society where no one will ever know when he's free from government surveillance"?

Ira Glasser, executive director of the New York Civil Liberties Union, said that he believed the cameras would be used not only for scanning, but would become "a permanent record, something to refer back to. Maybe identify somebody or arrest somebody. It then becomes a tool of general search and one must be against it!"

When it was pointed out that the police did not plan to videotape and store the films, Mr. Glasser replied, "Nonsense, if they're saying it's not permanent, they why are they doing it? It has no other virtue."

Responding to questions about a possible invasion of privacy, then Mayor John Lindsay said, "This is a public city, and the television cameras serve the same function as a patrolman on the beat. It's just out there watching the action."

This was the same John Lindsay who reviewed Alan Westin's *Privacy and Freedom* in the October 6, 1967, issue of *Life* magazine and said "Worst of all, lots of us are being tailed, bugged, probed, watched and tapped unawares without having any choice.''

It is a dilemma of no small proportions. Where does law enforcement end and invasion of privacy begin?

The following equipment is advertised and sold only to law-enforcement officers. Its supposed virtue is to deter and halt crime, and if it works *only* to that end, then we must agree that its use is justified. But who can be so sure that it will be? How can any assurance be given that the same equipment will not turn into another abused aspect of science?

Take for example the Vehicle Tracking System. How long will it be before a transmitter such as this system is built into every automobile that is sold—as a crime prevention device? As much a part of the "safety" system as seatbelts.

Vehicle Follower, Model 1012: "The Gus Model 1012 Vehicle Follower System features the latest innovations for complete vehicle surveillance. The system consists of an all-solid-state total-power degenerate interferometer receiver, a pair of quadraloop antennas, and a solid-state crystal-controlled transmitter.''

It features a receiver that is used in some rocket-tracking systems, and a Relative Direction Meter which tells you the direction of the car being followed either to the right or left of the surveillance car. (The range of the system is—in most cases—two or three miles.) For instance, when the car being followed turns to the right, the attached transmitter beams a signal back to the receiver, which indicates this by pointing to the right.

"The quadraloop receiver antennas are low profile antennas similar to the type used on sounding rockets. Their low profile, one inch high, allows them to be mounted on the hood of a vehicle with the guise of a hood ornament, or painted with acrylic paint to match the vehicle . . . or, for complete concealment, incorporated into a luggage rack atop the vehicle.''

There are two major types of transmitters, one of which can

1. Vehicle follower—receiving unit
2. Quadraloop receiving antennas
3. Transmitting unit of vehicle follower
4. Night-viewing device

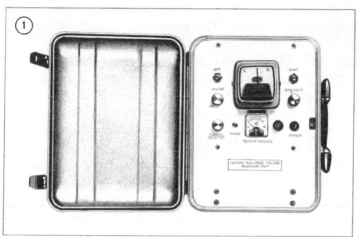

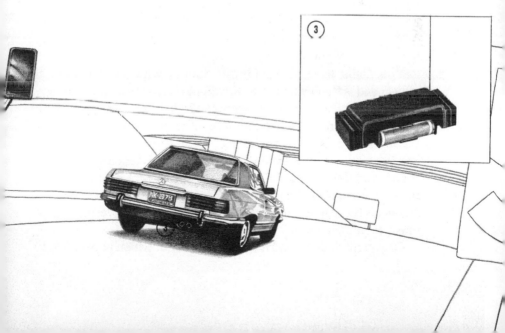

be attached to the bottom of a car (on the gas tank, for example) in just a few seconds. The other can be wired into the car permanently, with the car battery supplying the power, and the automobile's AM radio antenna used as a transmitting antenna. A diplexing junction box allows the AM radio antenna to be used for both.

The first transmitter comes with its own batteries, magnets, and short antenna, 7-1/4 inches. Its range is two or three miles, depending on the terrain. The permanent transmitter's range is about seven or eight miles.

Besides the Relative Direction Meter already described, there is a Relative Distance Meter which gives you some idea of how near you are to the transmitter.

O.K., let's say you have the Vehicle Tracking Device attached to a surveillance automobile. You have followed the victim successfully. He stops somewhere out in the hills of California, away from all city lights. It's night. There are no stars, no moon, no lights whatsoever. What do you do then? You can't aim your outdoor target microphone if you can't see where to aim it. Even though it gathers in sound waves and amplifies them a million times, when you finally do get zeroed in on your target, you might have lost too much time, and the important parts of the conversation may be over.

What you should have to go along with the Vehicle Tracking System is a Night Viewing Device:

You could have had a Find-R-Scope, which is an infrared viewer and is "compact . . . lightweight . . . easily adapted for any use. . . . It is used by the Photographic Industry for observing film development processes and handling of highly sensitive films. By the Electronics Industry for inspection of infrared-emitting diodes and laser applications. In Medical-Biological Science applications for nocturnal study of animals, mold studies on grain, and observations of various skin and vein conditions. By Law Enforcement Agencies for search and surveillance purposes and investigation of erasures and alterations to documents."

Or you might have had the Scan-R-Scope, which allows you to

"see in the dark without being seen." A Zeniscope—"The new generation is affordable"—could have been adapted to a closed-circuit TV system with an intensifier light-amplification of more than 25,000 power. (It can also be mounted on an M-16 rifle, M-14 rifle, M-60 machine gun, M-67 recoilless rifle, or M-79 grenade launcher.)

But let's say what you had finally decided on was a Night Viewing Device, Model 222, the lens of which collects and focuses the light, converting it in the viewer mechanism from light energy to electrical energy. It is then amplified and converted back into light energy. The reproduced image is then projected onto a screen at the rear of the unit. The operator can see this image with his eyepiece, or through the single-lens reflex camera, TV camera, or binocular viewer.

This model is called a "second-generation" device, since it offers a smaller size, very low distortion, and reduced blooming. Reduced blooming means that areas around bright lights—such as street lamps—which tended to "bloom" in the older versions, thereby reducing the vision of darker, unlighted areas—no longer do so. The operator can now view areas around these lights which were not observable before.

Night Viewing Devices are adaptable to TV cameras, 16-mm. motion-picture cameras, and 35-mm. photographic cameras for recording evidence through videotape recordings, motion picture film, or still photographs.

The reduced size and weight of the new model makes it very easy for it to be attached to the end of the camera, and the photographer will hardly be aware that he is holding anything more than his own camera. "Police officers will not be burdened with extra weight and can hold it steady for longer periods.

"Night Viewing Devices can be used with a binocular viewer for stake-outs from secluded areas. This viewer permits the observer to use both eyes while looking through the viewer, which is not as tiring. Also more than one observer can view the scene at the same time."

The Night Viewing Device, Model 222, with automatic brightness control, 75-mm. f/1.4 lens, focal plane-field iris, carrying case, batteries, and instruction manual, is $4,650.00.

We didn't show you pictures of the multitudes of tape recorders and transmitters, some of which are as small as a matchbook. We also didn't show you the amplifiers, multichannel monitors (for cell-block monitoring, detention rooms, hospitals, and defense installations), the electronic voice actuators, the many available cameras, both movie and still, or the Emergency Communications Van which some police departments now operate, notably the Maryland State Police.

When the appropriation for the ECV was approved, it was slated to be spent for an armored vehicle. "However, the consensus at the time of purchase was that armored units might provoke touchy situations to violence; consequently, a harmless-looking camper was chosen."

In an article appearing in the February 1973 *Police Chief* magazine, the van was described. Besides the communications setup—transceivers, teletype, standard telephone, a phone patch that can be quickly connected to existing phone lines, etc.—the Van contains video recorders, a video monitor, and a specially mounted Polaroid camera. "The photograph is then placed on the facsimile for identification at some remote location. The facsimile information can be routed either via radio or telephone lines, depending on the situation."

Hopefully the Van and others like it will be used for its designed purpose: "a concerted attack upon crime and to discover better methods of assisting people during natural calamities." Certainly efforts in this direction shouldn't be discouraged. Should they?

Certainly none but the very paranoid could imagine an American government so corrupted that such vans would be mobilized to contain and control the very citizens they were designed to protect.

Chapter Four:

How to Kill a Bug

"Can the average citizen make sure that he's not being bugged? Probably not, say the professionals, unless he is prepared to throw out his telephone, television, and other electronic instruments. He should then hold all sensitive conversations in the shower. The sound of the water playing on a shower curtain defeats all known bugs—so far."—Time *magazine, July 30, 1973*

The first thing you should remember in the antibugging game is that old adage, "An ounce of prevention is worth a pound of cure."

Lock your doors securely. Your file cabinets. Your wall safes, your strong boxes. Install burglar alarms. ·

Of course, you can't lock out contact mikes, harmonica bugs, and laser microphones. And you can't prevent someone from photographing you through solid walls. But you can lock out those bugs which have been planted. And you can lock your private papers away from private eyes. If you have good enough locks.

For your private papers—if you wish to keep them at home—the Lift Alarm Security Box is a good buy. It is made of steel, equipped with an alarm, a keylock, or two heavy combination locks, and weighs seven pounds. Somebody might be able to carry it away, but if their interest was in just photographing your documents, without your being aware of it, this box will prevent that. It sells for about thirty dollars at Hammacher Schlemmer in New York City.

As far as locking your front door goes, there are countless locks in all sizes and shapes, from the most simple to the most futuristically advanced.

In the permanent exhibit in the reading room of the Mechanics Institute in New York City is ample evidence of man's constant quest for personal security. It is a history—of sorts—of the "distrust thy neighbor" syndrome, with locks of all varieties. Among those on display are Egyptian locks, massive Renaissance locks, ancient Coptic keys, prison locks, alphabetical locks, a magic key lock, a grasshopper key lock, early electric locks, and one of the most curious locks going—a liquid time-lock with a two-chamber cylindrical case and a small opening by which liquid passed from chamber to chamber. It worked, but not nearly as well as the time locks on today's bank vaults.

The Institute also furnishes a book, *The Lure of the Lock*, to visitors for the asking. The book not only displays more beautifully wrought and ingenious locks, but it also explains how they work. Not that they're giving away any trade secrets, for anyone with a modicum of mechanical skill could soon learn how a given lock works and how to make it open without the correct key.

Then again you could always hire a pro. There is no dearth of trained lockpickers running around the country. Think of all those soldiers who went to the Army's Intelligence school at Fort Holabird, Maryland, and learned the fine techniques of lockpicking. There are many such intelligence schools, and most of them teach their personnel the same techniques. They don't have all that knowledge erased from their brains when they get a discharge, retire, or otherwise leave the employment of the intelligence services. It's still there, with the potential of being used after they become hungry, private citizens.

Unfortunately, all of this means that with today's burglar tools and armies of educated, ingenious lockpickers, it is highly unlikely that any of those available locks, no matter how complex, will keep out the most persistent invader. However, there are some locks and alarms available today that, if not *entirely* burglarproof, will give such uninvited snoopers as—say—the White House plumbers a violent case of the fits.

For example, the Identi-Lock made by Eaton Yale & Towne (4315 Bell Boulevard, Bayside, New York) which sells for approximately one hundred dollars, is now available to private citizens. It wasn't always. Originally it was used by the government to secure official national secrets. The lock works on the principles behind the new math. (If you don't know what that is, ask one of your kids or the delivery boy.) The lock consists of a binary-coded key and a factory-programmed logic panel. An optional alarm circuit can be fitted to signal the insertion of an alien key or other object. Powered by a battery or other external power source, the Identi-Lock should make you feel safe and secure—well, safer, anyway.

Another good lock alarm is made by 3M. In fact, the lock is called just that: Lock Alarm. With this slightly less expensive —sixty-five dollars plus installation—system, you know full well when you're routed from a sound sleep by invaders that they haven't made full penetration yet. The dead-bolt lock and chain is coupled to a highly sensitive solid-state, battery-powered electronic alarm. Any attempts to pick it or force it will cause a pulsating audio signal to go off, which will probably scare you as much as it does the lockpicker.

There are alarms for every possible problem, offering point protection (a front door), area protection (the whole house), or perimeter protection (the fence around the yard and house). The alarms are specifically made for houses, vaults, factories, or almost anything or anywhere you wish to install them. There are alarms which alert you, the police, a vigilance committee, or the entire neighborhood.

One alarm which could possibly alert an entire city—and would probably drive you deaf and dumb before you could shut it off—is the *Klaxton Alarm*. Used by the Air Force at military airports, (it could probably be picked up through an Army-Navy surplus store) it has that piercing "Whoop! Whoop!" sound which you've probably heard in war movies as all the pilots go scrambling out of their bunks and make a run for their planes. The alarm had to be loud enough to be heard above the roar of a medium-sized war and is made especially to be heard above the sound of fifteen B-52s warming up.

Imagine having one of those alarms attached to your front door. You'd probably never, ever, be robbed, but the neighbors might chase you away with large stones if it went off more than once.

But you needn't go that far. Probably a good compromise between practical limitations and an increased desire for protection is the Electronic Vibration Detector. Calculated to catch even the light tread of a cat burglar, it is computerized to let loose a host of alarms at the wrong vibration. The only drawback may be that the whole family could be terrified out of their wits by the head of the household's staggering up to the front door, hazily fiddling with the wrong key.

If you'd like something more soothing and less jangling, consider the Sonus Switch, an electronic gadget available from Hammacher Schlemmer, which is also sensitive to noises. It can be hooked up to any household appliance up to 750 watts, set to turn on whatever you hook it up to when a certain unusual noise is made.

The smart thing to do, of course, would be to hook it to a lamp or radio. But the perverse thing to do would be to set it up with a stereo system all set to play Alice Cooper's "Million Dollar Baby" at full blast. Imagine the look on the startled bugger's face when he treads softly into your quiet, dark living room, bumps against the lamp, and Alice Cooper screams obscenities at him. We'll bet that small telephone transmitter never gets planted in your telephone, after all.

Any or all of the above locks and alarms are good investments (the Sonus Switch is about twenty dollars) if you want a relatively secure feeling whether at home or away. You can at least feel confident that whatever is happening to your private home and papers while you're away is happening under great duress.

In addition to the alarms and locks, you can exploit the tools of the bugger's trade to your own advantage. Take the "infinity mike," for instance. If you want one, what you'll probably order is a Remote Audio Alert (RAA). (It changes its name when used as antisurveillance equipment, supposedly to protect the innocent.)

"Have the confidence of being able to check your premises from any telephone," reads the blurb for the RAA. "When the RAA is connected to your telephone, you can check your premises by listening for intruders or unusual sounds and monitor up to three alarm conditions from any other telephone. Some of the many locations in which the RAA may be used include apartments, homes, banks, business installations, industrial sites, vacation homes, offices, schools, sickrooms, and pharmacies. It can be used, also, for functions such as augmenting existing alarm systems, plant security, and even babysitting."

The RAA, however, incorporates an automatic disconnect after one minute—which, of course, is to your advantage. Somebody has to pay for the phone call since the line would constantly stay open if you didn't have the automatic disconnect. Another advantage of the RAA is that it can be used with other systems. It can be set—"upon interrogation"—to alert you when the temperature is below freezing, or notify you if the electrical power is off.

But its biggest selling point is security (actually, it's biggest selling point is bugging, but we're talking about defense right now). Coupled with an optional alarm system, you can tell from a simple phone call whether the alarm has been tripped.

"It may be used anywhere one wishes to use a telephone to detect unusual sounds—such as, the shuffling of secret papers, the sound of footsteps, hushed conversation or the like," the ad copy for Technical Communications Corporation (422 Marrett Road, Lexington, Mass. 02173) suggests.

Sounds throughout an area the size of a medium-size house can be picked up by the RAA. The actual working area depends on whether or not there are obstructions (such as walls) and whether or not you employ optional remote microphones.

With the RAA attached to your telephone, you can also have friends and neighbors call and make spot checks for you. The only thing you have to remember is to turn the RAA off when you're at home. Just think of all the fun your friends and neighbors could have dialing your number in the middle of a loud domestic quarrel so they could listen in unobtrusively.

Another surveillance item which doubles as antisurveillance gear is the closed-circuit television camera. Remember when it was watching you without your knowing it? Well, now you can set one up, conceal it with a fake book-jacket, perhaps the one on this book, and sit back to watch someone setting up a TV camera to watch you.

You can use the closed-circuit camera for surreptitious surveillance of your own premises from almost anywhere. Outside, inside, stairways, hallways, factories, offices, you name it. Of course, someone will have to be awake to watch the monitor, which could be a drawback.

All of the foregoing—available to the average citizen—was designed to help you stop the bugger before he has bugged. But how do you detect and stop the privacy-invaders if they have already penetrated your defenses and are now listening and watching you as you gloat over your wide-awake alarm system and your nonenter locks and your RAA and your closed-circuit television camera?

How do you know if you've killed the bug after the bug has already bitten?

You could always get yourself a portable automatic telephone-tester kit. Then you can actually check your own telephones for bugs. "Quickly, thoroughly rings the bugs out of the phone and lines," claims the manufacturer, F. G. Mason Engineering, Inc. (1700 Post Road, Fairfield, Conn. 06430) Among the many advertised features are these:

*Tests single, five, or seventeen-line call-directors without external attachments.
*Tests every wire connection for audio.
*Has a digital voltmeter read-out.
*Has an automatic tone-sweep with automatic disconnect and alarm.
*Is also surprisingly fast. A complete test of a five-line key-set takes only about twenty minutes. The kit weighs only twenty pounds and includes an attaché case.

One of the phenonomenal technical aspects of the testers is the "all wire—listen in" feature. This test automatically compares each individual wire with all other possible wire-combinations to detect room conversations being transmitted through the telephone wires. In the six-button business phone there are 1,275 combinations which can be used, while in the eighteen-button call-director, there are as many as 11,628 combinations. The wire being tested is identified by a numeric display. All fifty wires and the phone plug cover of a five-line key phone are tested in less than one minute.

The kit is designed for debugging only telephones and not any of the other microphones which might be planted around a certain area. If you are more inclined to do a complete sweep than to limit yourself to a simple phone check, what you need is the Saber CM-300 Countermeasure System. (Saber Laboratories, Inc., 1150 Bryant Street, San Francisco 94103) This kit is billed as a "defense against clandestine eavesdropping devices." It provides a complete basic countermeasure capability. Among these are:

*Detection of devices which use power or telecommunication lines as signal paths (radio, telephone, TV, etc.)
*Detection of wireless transmitting devices.
*Detection of any alteration or bypass technique employed against a standard telephone, regardless of whether it is a receiving bug or transmitter, or if additional microphones are used.

*Trace wire pairs through walls or other obstructions in order to determine termination or point of origin.
*Determination of presence of microphones or unidentified wires regardless of the type employed. This is important because carbon microphones or solid-state devices are detected by an ordinary amplifier only if they are active at the time the tests are being conducted.
*Activation of microphones detected on wires so that their exact location can be pinpointed.

This "countermeasure system" is designed for use by security officers, presumably at factories and office buildings. That's not saying that you—as a private homeowner or small businessman—can't lay your hands on one, but it will probably be more difficult.

Your best bet if you suspect you're being monitored is to hire an expert to debug your premises or offices. Mason Technical Security Services (a division of F. G. Mason) is one such firm which offers qualified, fully trained and equipped professionals who perform technical security surveys on either a onetime or a continuous basis.

Admittedly, the service is designed for places larger than a private home or small business. Industrial security on large complexes is their forte, but if you want to pay the freight, the service is available to you also.

Their pamphlet "Don't Read This Out Loud" describes their specialties, which include a complete electronic and physical sweep of your plant and executive offices. Often included in their sweep is a search for bugs in the private homes of the executives of the company involved. Some of these latter searches have yielded results.

Case histories of "bugged" or allegedly bugged industries include the El Paso Natural Gas Company; Hazel Bishop; Amphenol Corporation of Oakbrook, Illinois; Tech Torch Company of Carlstadt, New Jersey; and Schenley Industries.

In *The Third Listener* by John M. Carroll, the Hazel Bishop wiretapping was described: A cosmetics competitor was spying on new-product conferences in the New York offices of the Hazel Bishop company. The results of an electronic sweep of the offices disclosed that Raymond Spector, then president of Hazel Bishop, had not only his office and conference rooms bugged, but his home telephone and the phones in his residential hotel as well.

The information received from these bugs was said to have cost Hazel Bishop over $30 million in lost business in a single year. The reason was that the rival company used the tap reports to reach the market ahead of Hazel Bishop—sometimes as much as six weeks ahead—with an identical product.

Mason says that these losses could have been prevented through the use of its sweep services. It also quotes in its booklet from *Industrial Security* to reinforce the idea that its services are indispensable if a company wishes to protect its product research departments from compromise:

> The average American tends to think that eavesdropping is something that happens to the other fellow. It could not possibly happen to him. It is this naive attitude that makes electronic eavesdropping an easier task for the business or industrial spy. Additionally, many people think that the act of "bugging" a room or "tapping" a telephone is some sort of mysterious magic. Actually, nothing could be further from the truth. Anyone who has used a tape recorder or a high fidelity set, has used some of the basic components of eavesdropping systems. . . . Unless these [company] leaders get their heads out of the sand and face the problem squarely, electronic eavesdropping is liable to become even more of a menace to them.

Another company that feels the same way about industrial spying is Burns International Security Services. Its ad appearing in the October 1973 issue of *Security World* bore the headline, "Five Schemes to Steal Your Company from Under Your Nose." The five schemes are Bugging, Dishonest Employees, Corporate Spies, Insurance Fraud, and Theft in Transit.

Under Bugging, the ad stated that "a hidden microphone the size of this letter 'O' can broadcast next year's marketing plans to your competition. . . . Our confidential investigators are skilled at protecting your business or residence from wiretaps, concealed microphones and cameras. So don't worry about picking up your phone the next time it rings. Burns has an answer."

Burns also says that its "prehiring checks include employee fingerprinting, character and financial responsibility assessments, plus continuing post-hiring appraisals of employees. Burns has an answer."

Other answers from Burns include uniformed guards, crowd-control specialists, and undercover professionals to "infiltrate and report their impartial observations"—all tailored to fit the company's needs and checkbook.

"Last year theft cost American business $16 billion—a good part of it due to security leaks," according to Burns.

If you had chosen Mason Technical Security Services to do a sweep of your premises, its "technical survey" would have included the following three-stage operation:

1 An electromagnetic sprectrum search using sensitive bug-finding detectors.
2 A physical and electrical analysis of the telephone system, including the telephone itself, its wiring and appearance such as junction boxes. The electrical check uses a telephone analyzer which has an audio sweep generator, a low- and high-voltage pulse test-set, and a line linkage test-set.
3 A complete physical search which will disclose the presence of any "wire and mike" device as well as any defunct

electronic equipment which may have been in use in the past, but which no longer functions because of battery failure.

But even with all this, Mason admits that there is no way to guarantee that a room or facility is absolutely "cleaned" of eavesdropping equipment. "Just as in physical security where there is no absolute protection against intruders, there is no positive way of assuring absolute privacy short of a specially built room which is guarded twenty-four hours a day."

Besides a room within a room and the twenty-four-hour-a-day guard, to be absolutely certain that you are not being bugged, you should also employ scramblers, jamming devices, bug detectors and a lot of time, money, and loss of spontaneity.

Speaking of devices that jam transmitters, experts say that although impressive demonstrations may be made with these devices, they are usually ineffective in actual operation, because there are new electronic devices which can be used to overcome the "white noise" produced by the jammers.

There are also telephone or voice scramblers "for maximum protection against telephone eavesdropping." Sirchie Fingerprint Laboratories produces a unit which consists of a pair of scramblers preset with a specific mixing code that only the "two parties involved in the telephone coversation can interpret. The scramblers can be ordered with additional pre-coded units if required. Used extensively by military intelligence agencies. Complete with batteries and instructions." The price of Sirchie's scrambler is $690.00 per pair. Additional units are $350.00 each.

Technical Communications Corporation makes Multicode Voice Privacy Systems in different models. One of them, Model 105, is a combined speaker/microphone and scrambler for personal radios. "It is compatible with all types of frequency inversion scrambler systems or can be made non-compatible." The 207 series is more complicated, containing over one million code combinations. It can be used with AM and FM radios and for telephone applications.

So how effective is a scrambler? As effective as a jam, apparently, because no matter how sophisticated, the scrambling code can still be broken, either by listening, taping and replaying, or by other electronic means. The more sophisticated the scrambler, the more difficult to break the code, of course, but the scrambler at this level is more susceptible to distortions and interference in transmission.

"As a general rule, a voice privacy system will not require more than 1000 to 2000 effective codes to provide over twenty-four hours of security from someone with a similar device who is trying to guess the code being used," according to TCC.

Twenty-four hours? Well, maybe that's better than nothing, but it seems like an awfully lot of trouble for such a short time.

Maybe the best way to kill a bug is just to use one of the two methods employed by Carl Bernstein and Bob Woodward—the enterprising Washington *Post* reporters—when they talked about their investigation of Watergate in Woodward's apartment. They turned up the radio to a very high volume and then turned on a shower directing the water against the curtain.

And they never, ever told their secrets over the telephone.

Chapter Five:

The Trail You Leave

"A government investigator, regardless of where he is, is going to go to any source of information that is open. If I have no trouble going into your bank account, I'm going to go into your bank account, and to your neighbor if your neighbor will talk. If a source of information is available, our investigator is going to use it. Otherwise he'll look elsewhere. If the libraries don't want to make information available, this is their prerogative."
—Harold Sear, speaking for the Internal Revenue Service, in reaction to disclosures that the IRS was asking public libraries to release their records of book borrowers.

Although sophisticated electronic surveillance of American citizens is no rare event within the nation's military and civilian intelligence communities, the majority of us have little to fear from this use of surreptitious electronic and supersnooper technological hardware. One of the reasons is that it really isn't needed. American citizens as a rule have already surrendered all the information that an investigator would want anyway.

In forgotten school records, job applications, IQ and aptitude tests, passport application information, credit records, bank statements, insurance reports, ad nauseam, we have left the story of our lives behind us. All ready and waiting, not for the superspy

75

of technology, but for the methodical and plodding Sherlock Holmes, who picks up a clue here and a clue there and pieces them all together like a jigsaw puzzle.

Just as your library records will reveal a little of what interests you by the books you check out (the IRS evidently believed that discovering which elements of our culture were checking out "subversive literature" would help trap tax-dodgers), so thousands of other innocent records will reveal a little more about you with each scrap of information you leave behind. And when the Sherlock Holmes assigned to you pieces them together, he will have a portrait of a human being which officially will be a "true" one, whether it is the real you or not.

What's more, such scraps of information may even include information about sexual aberrations, drinking habits, and drug use and/or abuse. The information—to add a little spice to your official portrait—may be totally inaccurate or out of date.

James Millstone, former Washington correspondent for the St. Louis *Post-Dispatch*, discovered just how difficult it is to challenge such information. Preparing to move back to St. Louis, he routinely asked his insurance agent to transfer his automobile coverage to a local broker.

The new company rejected the application.

Millstone was surprised. He had an excellent driving record and a responsible position with one of the country's leading newspapers. Surely his reputation (and, most important he thought, his record,) could not be questioned.

The credit-reporting firm hired by his insurer didn't think much of his reputation. He was a "hippie type," they reported; suspected of being a drug user; had a history of apartment evictions; was troubled by lack of judgment and a bad attitude; participated in a peace demonstration; was disliked by his neighbors and had unruly and uncontrollable children.

It was all false—either the product of an investigator's fertile imagination or the result of a single interview with a neighbor the Millstones didn't get along with. Of course, no mention was made of his driving record. Evidently no dirt was uncovered there. Of course, that *was* what the investigation was supposed to be all about.

Millstone got the insurance, but is suing the credit firm for damages, contending that additional false material is included in his files.

The case of James Millstone is not unusual.

John Gregg, a veteran insurance man, speaking before a Senate investigating subcommittee on consumer credit in late 1973, said that at least 40 percent of all information filed on individuals because of life insurance, health and accident coverage, and consumer credit applications is "defective and erroneous." Gregg, who is also a former FBI agent further said that under existing federal law private individuals—the consumers—are powerless to discover if such defective records exist on themselves or to correct them if they do happen to find out.

The subcommittee before which Gregg testified was looking into loopholes in the Fair Credit Reporting Act of 1971. This law was the first major break for the consumer making the gathering of private information by credit and insurance investigators on consumers more difficult, and also giving consumers the right to force disclosures of their records. However, there was one major loophole in the law: A person's medical history was exempted from disclosure.

This loophole has been a boon for insurance companies. For example, it was disclosed that the Union Fidelity Life Insurance Company of Philadelphia denied a claim by one of its insurees in 1972 because, the company said, "the records we obtained indicated that this condition pre-existed the effective date of your policy. Since these records are confidential, we are unable to advise you of the information we have."

Mrs. Lola Gene Jackson, a widow who operates a small real estate firm on St. Simons Island, Georgia, has sought to force the insurance company to open their files. But all in vain. Meanwhile she is out more than two hundred dollars.

Reports of other insurance investigations' "confidential medical" reports confirm the fact that Union Fidelity of Philadelphia was not the only company to use the medical loophole. One company had asked for a more complete investigation of a woman's moral character based on the "medical information" that she had given birth to an illegitimate child. Another ordered further "medical" checks on an applicant because friends had said that the applicant customarily "drank three martinis before dinner."

The Medical Information Bureau of Stamford—which has been described by Dr. Sidney M. Wolfe, a consumer advocate in the health field, as a "medical CIA"—contains data on 11 million people, including information about their sex lives, drinking patterns, and drug use, plus "medical" data on such hazardous hobbies as auto racing and flying.

Mr. Joseph C. Wilberding, executive director of the MIB, told the Senate subcommittee that the sources of such information came from credit investigations, doctors, physical examinations given by the companies, and the individual policyholders themselves. Mr. Wilberding said that the applicants were not told that the information they revealed might be made available to hundred of companies that support MIB, and furthermore insisted that the applicants, "shouldn't be told." For such disclosure, in his words, "could possibly interfere with the sale of the policy by the salesman, and would result in more paperwork."

The MIB's records and disclosures are just some of the many we have left behind us—to be used and abused by the companies and individuals obtaining them. For example, take your name. Names are the least sacred component of a person's personality, it seems. The names of 6.4 million New York State vehicle-owners were *sold* to a marketing service firm just a few years ago for the grand sum of $86,000. According to confidential sources, the practice is still going on, not only in New York State, but in other states as well.

When a citizen dared sue New York State, based on the contention that his name was personal property and could not be sold on the open market like a sack of potatoes, the presiding judge disagreed. One's name, he decided, was not "a person's property protected by the law." New York was free to treat it, sell it, bargain for it, or whatever, as the state saw fit.

The trail we leave can be started at an early age—and found in unusual places. Of the 64,000 narcotics-users reportedly on file with the Bureau of Narcotics and Dangerous Drugs on October 30, 1970, three were under the age of three years old. Although addiction was admittedly involuntary—the result of addicted mothers giving birth to equally addicted children—these infants can look forward to having this information on their records for the rest of their lives. A 1972 broadcast by the ABC television network, "The Littlest Junkie," showed that the three infants of 1970 had been joined by untold thousands of children only two years later. They too can look forward to a lifelong record of a permanent government file identifying them as "Reformed Narcotics Users."

Of course, the favorite identifier of police and intelligence agencies throughout the world is still the fingerprint. Although the earliest pronouncement that fingerprints could be used for identification was made in 1684, it wasn't until almost two centuries later, in 1860, that they were actually used in criminal detection. The English used them in India to trap natives who had developed a profitable trade forging marks entitling them to government allowances.

The ensuing decade has seen an increase in fingerprinting, now the acknowledged prime tool of identification. FBI files contain over 200,000,000 prints which represent, omitting duplicates, over 80,000,000 citizens. Over 30,000 prints arrive each day into the FBI's Washington, D.C. headquarters. In exchange for the prints, all of the information contained in their files is immediately sent back to the agency which initially submitted the prints.

Less than half of these agencies are engaged in the business of law enforcement. The rest of them are banks, insurance companies, credit companies, the military, the civil service, defense contractors, and employers with "sensitive" jobs. For a considerable time, the Bureau leaned so far toward the side of efficiency and data-accumulation that they actively solicited "donors" to submit their prints on a "protective measure" basis. Civic and business groups made a regular campaign out of it.

The fingerprints on file at the FBI headquarters will probably remain long after the fingerprinted one is dead, and most of us who have been fingerprinted for one reason or another have grown used to that fact. Yet one wonders if such efficient data-collection is really that vital to law enforcement. Scotland Yard, Britain's equivalent (in some ways) to the FBI, also has a large fingerprint file—of proven criminals *only*. If someone is arrested, fingerprinted, and eventually acquitted, the prints he left are purged from the files. Prints collected for any special investigations or other reasons are also quickly destroyed when they are no longer needed.

But in the United States, this is not the practice. It seems we hate to destroy a record once we have it. And this national propensity for instant identification has resulted in some noteworthy abuses, which always seem to involve children—who have little to say in the matter.

In Newark, New Jersey, in 1973, forty eighth-grade boys were ordered by a judge to submit to fingerprinting by police officials engaged in investigating the murder of a sixty-three-year-old man. The discovery of a class ring, pinpointing the school and the year of the possible assailant, was purportedly what prompted the decision after the police request for the fingerprinting. A lengthy court battle brought—and eventually won—by the enraged parents was the result.

In Maine, the identification game began even younger. Since the end of World War II, every fifth-grade pupil in the state has been fingerprinted annually for identification purposes. Representative Theodore S. Curtis, Jr., who had originally asked the legislature to permit parents to withhold their children from the program, later announced upon further researching for his bill, "that the entire program was unwise, if not unconstitutional . . . as a violation of the right to privacy." There was no opposition from the legislature's Education Committee when he asked that the program be banned immediately. And presumably it has been done.

In a way, the entire furor over fingerprinting is an anachronism, since new methods of instant identification are already beginning to displace the fingerprint. The newest and most promising method is based on the premise of fingerprinting; each person's print is unique and each person is thereby identifiable. This time the premise is applied to the voice which, researchers have discovered, is just as unique as the fingerprint. To most of us, this is a little hard to believe, especially after hearing impressionists mimic well-known personalities. But scientifically, each voice is absolutely different. The result of a sound produced by the vocal mechanism—throat, nasal, and mouth cavities—and the articulators—lips, teeth, tongue, soft palate, and jaw muscles—when analyzed by a spectrogram produces a picture of the voice. This picture does not drastically change even when disguises—such as a handkerchief over the phone—are employed. In fact, voiceprints are almost impossible to disguise. Nothing tested so far seems to change the pattern of the spectrogram—neither loss of teeth, aging, camouflaging, nor a mouthful of marbles. Mimics don't even come close to copying their model's patterns, though the differences of sound, the pattern, and even the pacing might prove indistinguishable to the ordinary untrained ear.

The voiceprint is well on its way to becoming a new tool of identification, and James C. Wright had the dubious distinction on May 28, 1966, of becoming the first person in the world to be convicted by a voiceprint. The twenty-five-year-old serviceman, stationed at Travis Air Force Base, was proven by voiceprinting to be guilty of making obscene phone calls to a young local resident. A recording of one of his obscene calls was subjected to the voice spectrogram and compared to a live spectrogram of Wright's voice. The dubious jurors were finally convinced after a detailed explanation which was reminiscent of the early efforts to allow fingerprint evidence to be introduced in court.

Thus, although its acceptance by judges, juries, and even the police is surprisingly recent, voiceprinting is currently being touted as superior to fingerprinting in many situations, which would lead us to predict an increase in law-enforcement wiretapping in order to obtain them. A new and successful technique of identification always seems to bring out the expansive dreams of the law-enforcement agencies which employ the new method. So not too surprisingly, a national file of voiceprints has been proposed by a number of identification experts. They would, according to plans currently taking shape, encode the ten most commonly used words (it, me, the, you, on, I, is, and, a, too) of all criminals as a start. One doubts, however, given the past history of "record-keeping overkill," that the FBI and local agencies would suddenly prove indulgent to temptations of restraint. In ten years, it seems likely, the voiceprint file, swelled by second-generation "donors," will surpass in number even the astronomically high figures of the FBI's fingerprint files.

It's an easy step from fingerprints and voiceprints to signatures as an identifying trail-leaving medium, especially in America, for everyone—at one time or another—signs on the dotted line.

The United States consumes much more of the earth's limited resources, and far more of the world's raw materials and products, than our population or size warrants—as the energy crisis has brought smartly home to us. To some, especially the hundreds of thousands of people starving in the less-developed countries of the world, there seems to be little justice in the ratio of our population to our consumption. But there is at least one group that doesn't seem to mind the gross imbalance; the companies who have specialized in supplying or keeping track of credit, an item which is very necessary to keep up our rate of consumption. The companies who specialize in the field of credit have—to employ the title of a recent bestseller—hooked onto the Billion Dollar Sure Thing.

Or rather, the $100 billion sure thing, since that's the estimate of credit transactions that took place in 1973. The corporations that survive only because of these credit transactions are the credit bureaus—hundreds of them across the country—which maintain the detailed dossiers on each person who is part of the $100 billion bonanza.

If you have ever bought anything on credit—which more than likely you have—you are probably one of the 110 million Americans whose files reside in the computers of the Associated Credit Bureaus of America's member firms.

None of these credit bureaus are required to be licensed in any of the fifty states, and they operate in all of them. Only one recently enacted bill covers any of their operations and minimally protects the information in their files. Nothing, however, neither laws nor scruples, stops the bureaus from selling records of credit buyers to creditors, landlords, employers or, for that matter, anyone with a "legitimate business interest." Selling and making money is, after all, their game. Protection of privacy is not.

In 1970, the Columbia Broadcasting System, as part of a proposed news report, set out to check just how confidential and difficult to purchase these records really were. They created a fictitious systems corporation and sent out requests for credit reports on their quickly imprinted stationery to twenty commercial credit bureaus. They asked for copies of files of individuals randomly chosen from the local telephone directory, citing their reasons for the request as "prospective employee."

Ten out of the twenty companies contacted—a rather startling 50 percent of the sample—responded immediately with the information requested. Another, seemingly a bit more careful, refused to divulge any information until they received a signed contract. The newsmen, ever ready to comply, dutifully signed the name of one of the fictitious company's equally fictitious officers. The information they had requested was immediately forthcoming.

One need not be a scholar to recognize that even a summary check of any of the eleven credit bureaus' files would have revealed the fraudulent claims of the CBS newsmen. It is equally obvious that none of those who so freely supplied the information made even a routine effort to establish the legitimacy of their potential client before revealing intimate details of twenty individuals' credit histories. Profit is evidently a far more tempting mistress than any stated business policy.

Profit is a mighty and alluring mistress and more than anything else, credit is big business. The Retail Credit Company, largest credit bureau in the country, needs 70,000 employees to keep track of its files on 50 million people and prepare more than 35 million reports each year. Credit Data Corporation, the runner-up, adds another 7 million reports per year. It also had another 27 million detailed dossiers on American citizens on file.

Most credit bureaus glean the information for their millions of files from any source that is immediately and easily available. News clippings are a prime source. Auto accidents, drunk driving charges, arrests, divorces, marriages, inheritances, bankruptcies—all eventually find their way into the back pages of America's newspapers. All of the details of these mishaps and celebrations eventually find their way into the credit files. Neighbors, friends, acquaintances, fellow employees, and employers also provide a lot of information about an individual that purports to be "fact." Yet, despite these "facts," on most credit bureau reports, the companies regularly include a disclaimer of responsibility, for example: "[The information in this file] has been obtained from sources deemed reliable, the accuracy of which [the respective credit bureau] does not guarantee." The information whose "accuracy" is not guaranteed, however, is regularly disseminated to anyone who pays for the report with the inference, simply by inclusion, that it *is* accurate. Little of it is ever checked. If a neighbor infers a drinking habit, as one bureau manager admitted to us, the allegation—unchecked, unreliable, and unsubstantiated—would be routinely added to the person's file. Gossip, innuendo, prejudice, and revenge can easily create "facts" which are routinely included in these files because of such a loose and irresponsible attitude.

Just how fiction is miraculously transformed into the "facts" of many files was explained at the February 1974 hearings of the Subcommittee on Consumer Credit of the Senate Committee on Banking, Housing and Urban Affairs. Four former investigators for Retail Credit testified that they were forced by the company to falsify credit reports and to meet "unrealistic" reporting goals —as high as twenty per day. Anyone who balked was quickly dismissed, they said.

All four stated that they were required to produce adverse information on a certain percentage of insurance applicants, anywhere from 6 to 10 percent. The vast majority of credit reports are on consumers applying for insurance.

This percentage of declinables, said Richard Riley, is then used to show that a particular agency is more "thorough" than another. "The one who can get more adverse information," he explained, "can net more contracts." Richard Riley spent fifteen years with Retail Credit in New York and Florida.

The former investigators also charged that Retail Credit frequently based reports on information from a single source. Their estimates of the percentage of such one-source checks ranged from 50 to 95 percent.

In one case, outlined by Len Holloway of Retail Credit's Miami office, a woman applying for auto insurance was rejected. She was reported to be a "a lady of the evening."

Mr. Holloway's personal check uncovered ten neighborhood interviews which all agreed that the woman was held in "high esteem." The only interviewee who differed from the consensus was the "neighborhood nut." She was, of course, the sole source of the allegation that had become an unquestioned fact in the woman's credit report. Not surprisingly, credit companies have almost unlimited access to law-enforcement files. Most of the information in a specific file will probably come from these agencies—local, state, or federal. Just as unsurprisingly, law-enforcement officials have practically unlimited access (*without* warrants) to the credit bureaus' information—in fact or fantasy —on millions of Americans. The largest user of these files—one might almost add, predictably—is the Federal Bureau of Investigation, which has been known to casually examine 25,000 reports in one day without the permission of the individual or a court warrant. The entire hand-in-glove operation between the credit industry and law-enforcement agencies becomes a maddening circle of inaccuracy, innuendo, and irresponsibility. The FBI makes its arrest records available to the credit bureau, which then adds it to the data already in its files. Since the FBI doesn't bother to update their records with regard to the dismissal of charges, upheld conviction, or any other disposition of the cases, the information supplied is of dubious value and validity. To this incomplete data, the credit bureaus mix in their own inaccurate information—news clippings with only partial information, unconfirmed reports from neighbors and friends, obsolete material or incorrect information due to computer transfer problems. This file, now a complex mixture, probably more fiction than fact, is the one that is then made available to law-enforcement agencies, which remove the information they require. The circle of irresponsibility is already complete and will continue to unwind, piling inaccuracy atop fantasy, ad infinitum.

Since this information is easily accessible and freely traded with other computer systems, protection of the files is almost nonexistent. Congress finally took at least the first step towards proper control of such unprotected data on April 25, 1971, with the passage of the Fair Credit Reporting Act. A kind of "Credit Bill of Rights," it places certain restrictions on the unshackled bureaus. Specifically, it gives each individual:

(a)   The right to be told the name and address of the "Consumer Reporting Agency" (credit bureau) responsible for any report which was used as a basis for denying credit.

(b)   The right "at any time for any reason" to be told the nature, substance, and source of any information (excluding medical information in full and the specific sources of "investigative information") collected by a Consumer Reporting Agency.

(c)   The right to obtain this information free of charge.

(d)   The right to be told who has received his credit report within the preceding six months (two years if the report was furnished for employment purposes).

(e)   The right to have information he believes to be incomplete or incorrect reinvestigated by the bureau and removed if proven inaccurate.

(f)   If information is deleted as a result of this action, the right to have the agency notify those he names of the deletion of previously received information.

(g)   The right to have his version of a disputed portion of an agency's report included in the permanent file and in all subsequent reports. Also the right to have his version sent to certain businesses who have previously received reports (for a reasonable fee).

(h)   The right to insure that the reports are withheld from anyone "without a legitimate business need."

(i)   The right to sue if the Consumer Reporting Agency willfully or negligently violates the law.

(j)   The right to be notified if a company is seeking information that could constitute an "investigative consumer report."

(k)   The right to request further information as to the nature and scope of the investigation and to be informed of the nature and substance of information already collected for the report.

This act does go further in some areas than is immediately apparent. It stipulates that the inclusion of all adverse information is subject to a seven-year limit, except for bankruptcies, which remain on file for fourteen years. The right to know all of the information on file is, of course, the most important protection the bill provides.

The attempt to exclude "sources of 'investigative information' '' from this provision is more rhetorical than practical. Since litigation can force the disclosure of the source's identity, the agency cannot guarantee confidentiality to amateur informants.

Unfortunately, the omissions are far more numerous than the excesses newly regulated by this legislation. While citizens now have the right to inspect and correct information in credit files (a right which hasn't exactly been advertised on television), they still cannot control access to that information or really control the nature or extent of the information that is included in the files. Similarly, although enforcement is provided for through private legal action, proving negligence by a credit bureau is something else again. The current massive growth of core-to-core (computer to computer) communication makes the files easily transferable. Where these files end up is still completely unregulated, and the transfers are still unreported. Most importantly, however, the many rights which the bill supposedly gives the average citizen are based on the premises that (a) he is aware of these rights, which have not received extensive publicity, and (b) he is sufficiently aware of the processes involved to institute the necessary requests to receive information, correct inaccurate data, etc. The bill leaves the onus for protection squarely on the shoulders of the citizens, not of the credit companies, where it belongs. Unless an individual requests the name and address of a company, it will not be provided. He will not be told the nature of the information on file, the identity of those who have received reports, or the nature and scope of a current investigation, without specifically requesting to be so informed. The credit companies themselves need never inform anyone of anything if nobody bothers to ask.

Insurance companies, with a need for current and personal information that rivals the credit industry, also rival the bureaus in their maintenance of inaccurate data, presented as fact. Insurance Inspection Agencies, however, have even less time to check the information they receive. Of course, the Fair Credit Reporting Act doesn't affect their practices. On the average, an inspector must process ten to fifteen reports a day. Assuming a typical eight-hour day, this would allow them to spend only a little more than a half hour on each inspection report, including the time spent writing it and transportation time. It is highly unlikely that sufficient care can be exercised with such pressure constantly on the investigator. Routine inclusion of "soft data" (gossip), with no attempt at verification, is an obvious result. Of course, the lack of time to substantiate any investigative allegations leads to the automatic inclusion of information "pulled" from biased informants or even "revenge reports" prepared by vindictive inspectors.

According to confidential sources in a representative agency, there is a monthly quota established for declines, referring to persons whose business is not accepted because of certain derogatory information that investigation has allegedly uncovered. Since a certain percentage of each month's applicants *must* be rejected, enough information to even slightly support the declines must be dug up, or at the very least, invented, by an inspector who needs a few more declines at the end of the month. According to our sources, the quota for that company was 8 percent for life insurance and 12 percent for automobile coverage. Naturally the quotas are officially nonexistent, but they are very practically followed and enforced.

Just to insure that the information they collect remains totally *un*confidential, most insurance companies rarely do their own claims work. According to John Healey, a top investigator of the CNA insurance group, it is common practice for the companies to give out their claims-detecting work to private detective firms. Their files, containing many of the details of an individual's life, as well as unconfirmed but possibly damaging allegations, thus become virtually public property, shuttled from investigator to investigator.

As Senator Sam Ervin drily remarked, Americans "are constantly being intimidated, coerced or pressured into revealing information to the wrong people, for the wrong purposes at the wrong time.'' The information-gathering begins innocently enough, when the child first enters grade school. He or she rarely sees the collectors coming. Yet, as a result of testing, probing, and questioning, generations of Americans have gone through school dogged by awesome dossiers of scholastic and personal information most have never seen: their official school records.

The school record of each person begins when the pupil first enters school. As the youngster grows, so does the file, following along from grade to grade, even to other schools. Containing far more than merely the academic records of the pupil, this all-inclusive compendium will eventually include personality and behavior data; all official scores on IQ achievement, and personality tests; medical reports; and other detailed records, including even psychological and psychiatric records and the comments of teachers and guidance counselors.

A 1967 conference on the ethical and legal aspects of school recordkeeping was sponsored by the Russell Sage Foundation. The participants declared that ''deficiencies in record keeping policies, taken together, constitute a serious threat to individual privacy in the United States.'' A number of practices and serious omissions leave the entire system open to abuse. Few pupils, and fewer parents, really know what information is contained in these records. Rarely, even if they eventually discover the extent of the information that has been systematically gathered and filed, do they have the right to challenge erroneous or prejudicial data in these files. Parents and children have given up their right to privacy, inadvertently yet completely. Few realize they couldn't look at their own children's records if they wished. Most are under the false assumption that such is their right. Yet the schools, while not allowing such perusal, ostensibly because the records are confidential, fail to safeguard adequately the confidential records from examination by unauthorized school personnel and handle outside requests for access to information from the files on a strictly ad hoc basis.

New York State has gone furthest in attempting to rectify the horrible state of affairs, enabling parents to exert at least a modicum of supervision over school officials. In 1960, the State Education Department decided that parents were entitled to see progress reports, results of personality and IQ tests and other parts of their child's records. This was later extended by State Education Commissioner Ewald B. Nyquist, who declared that parents had the right to see even informal data, such as teachers' comments and the notes of guidance counselors, as well as the official records. Eventually, the school system gave parents the right to challenge derogatory information. Now the material can even be expunged if it is proven inaccurate or unfair. This decision was part of a policy statement which further declared that (a) sample forms of all student records must be made available to the public, insuring its knowledge of the types of information being collected from its school-age children; (b) before collecting any information from students, "informed" parent consent is required, and greater protection must be given school records to prevent abuse due to unauthorized review.

As extensive as these provisions appear on the surface, they are still woefully inadequate. Although they greatly extended parental supervision and administrative responsibility, they completely overlooked the content of the files themselves. More and more, younger and younger, schoolchildren are being subjected to batteries of intelligence quotient (IQ), psychological, and behavioral data tests. The results could shape the children's lives much more than we might suspect. On one hand, the high IQ child will probably receive endless further testing, honors classes, and special courses, all designed to encourage the active use of what is, after all, merely a *potential* suggested by the test. Or, if he is truly brilliant, he might wind up nestled in the West Virginia foothills with 99 other children (two from each state) for intensive seminars.

Each summer these selected representatives come to the ten-year-old National Youth Science Camp, now on a fifteen-acre site and a nationally respected meeting ground for young talent. IBM lends computer equipment; the National Radio Astronomy Observatory, located nearby, provides lecturers, and the counselors are experts in such fields as high-energy physics, crystallography, and computer languages. "Camp IQ," as it has been dubbed, is a valuable training-site for future leaders.

But not everyone is blessed with test scores that place her or him at near-genius level. For those less blessed, the result is far removed from the special classrooms and bucolic meanderings in West Virginia. Just one year ago, the New York State Supreme Court ruled that four-year-old twin girls must be placed for adoption because their mother's intelligence quotient was too low. She was, according to the court, unable to give them proper care and attention. The 8—0 ruling ordered that the parent-child relationship between David and Diane McDonald and their daughters, Joyce and Melissa, must be legally terminated.

The court said the mother came from "a very cruel and immoral home," but cited no other reasons for the decision except for her "very low IQ," tested at 47. Mr. McDonald's test score was 74. The Court decided that Mrs. McDonald simply "did not have the ability to care for the children or the capacity of a person with normal intelligence to love and show affection."

The court's decision concluded that "[even though] considerable improvement has occured in her ability to keep house, there still remains a serious doubt as to Diane's ability to cope with the situations requiring guidance and to perform those things a mother must do in raising children. . . . Although the father is able to do considerably better, the best interest of the twins requires a termination to him as well."

Thus the result of a test was the primary factor in taking away the McDonald's children to live in a series of foster homes, unable to be with their own parents. Can any test really be so certain and unchallengeable as to form a proper basis for such action by a court? IQ test scores can fluctuate as much as thirty points because of age, environmental influences during the testing, nervousness, or many other difficult-to-pinpoint variables.

These IQ scores form only a small part of a typical child's records these days. Aptitude and personality tests are almost a regular part of the yearly curriculum in many schools. The tests are subject to myriad abuses, however, on a number of fronts. The variety of tests a school or employer (industry is using personality tests on an increasingly wider scale to screen applicants) can use are staggering: There are presently well over five hundred personality tests and inventories, with hundreds of questions in each. This vast variety, and the different specific uses of certain tests, can easily lead interpreters of the results astray. The "wrong" test given to the wrong person in the wrong situation will never result in proper scores, since a test *must* be properly selected for each particular person and situation. Even in very similar situations, the same test may be appropriate for one and wholly inadequate for another. Tests which have proven invaluable in one company's main offices are totally worthless in a local branch of the same firm.

Even if the proper test is administered, as one executive succinctly remarked, "To know how validly the test predicts, a follow-up study is required." In other words, inventors of these various personality inventories cannot guarantee the validity or accuracy of their brainchild's results. The only sure way to discover any correlation is to check later behavior and see whether it matches predictions from the tests.

Despite this inherent lack of validity and accuracy, tests proliferate. Indeed, more are being produced each year and are quickly snapped up by "progressive" educators, industrialists, and executives, supposedly to discover what makes a certain pupil/employee/executive candidate "tick." The questions on most tests vary from general opinions and those designed to elicit background information to the following examples (to be answered Yes or No), part of the Cornell Index battery of tests:

(a)   Does worrying continually get you down?

(b) Do you usually have trouble in digesting food?

(c) Are you keyed up and jittery every moment?

(d) Are you a sleepwalker?

Some tests get far more intimate and far less careful. The Minnesota Multiphasic Personality Inventory test, put out by the Psychological Corporation, is scored entirely by computer. A clinical-interpretive analysis is sent to a client after the proper forms have been submitted. The entire analysis is performed *solely* by the computer; a psychologist never sees the test, the results or the analysis.

Another aspect of the school testing programs recently led to an explosion in the New York City newspapers. Board of Education President Seymour P. Lachman accused the United States Office of Education of attempting to establish a double standard of school testing—one for black and Hispanic children, and another for whites. He branded the agency "discriminatory" and charged that they had seriously violated the intent of Congress. The agency's actions, Lachman said, are "a revival of the notorious separate but equal system—now applied to testing. It is in essence a system of condescension and bigotry that assumes non-white children are unable to learn."

The uproar, dredging up the whole question of just how culturally biased school tests really were, occurred because of an USOE "experiment" involving approximately one hundred school systems, with a separate test for "minority" children. According to its own correspondence, the USOE discussed "developing a mathematics and reading test specifically tailored to the minority isolated school."

New York City school officials now contend that Chicago, Cincinnati, and Pittsburgh are having "deep reservations" about continued participation. The incident prompting the eruption from both sides of the fence was the withdrawal of $964,000 in previously allocated federal funds to School District 19 (East New York) because, according to Lachman, "it did not want to be a party to discrimination against children on the basis of race or ethnic origins." The money spent for District 19 has since been returned to the Treasury Department.

Lachman charged that the experiment "is really trying to say that minority children are so different they cannot compete in learning when placed alongside other youngsters. I have read and re-read the USOE's rationale. But I must admit that I find it entirely unacceptable, contradictory and based upon the concept of dual standards.

"I believe . . . that any healthy child—whether he lives in Bayside or Bedford-Stuyvesant—can be taught to master fundamental learning skills and compete with other children, despite differences in race or other origin. The Board of Education accepts this premise and believes that every student, regardless of race, religion, or ethnic origin or socioeconomic background, can succeed academically.

"Furthermore, all the children have a right to succeed alongside of their fellow students and to be evaluated by the same standards that apply to all other members of the pupil populations."

Although the program had previously been announced by the government as "voluntary," federal officials said the commitment to New York had been reversed in June and they therefore had every right to withdraw the funds. In conjunction with Lachman's charge that the USOE was developing "a discriminatory test that established minority norms," the central school board released correspondence and telegrams outlining the development of the controversial incident. The almost $1 million in federal grants were evidently revoked when District 19 told officials it would not be a part of its program of "unequal and discriminatory testing." According to this correspondence, USOE officials were attempting to establish "minority norms" specifically to *remove* "test biases." They wanted to develop "a less biased and more sensitive instrument" to measure the effectiveness of special education programs for inner city schools. Michael J. Wargo of the USOE's Office of Planning, Budgeting and Evaluation said that as of June 20, 1973, "cooperation has been received" and testing completed in 94 of the 100 randomly selected school-systems.

Such experiments raise serious questions about not only the cultural bias inherent in current tests but also the propriety, given this built-in bias, of attempting to circumvent the problem by establishing norms for segments of the school system rather than for the system as a whole. Treating bias by legitimizing it and incorporating it into the system—calling it merely the establishment of "minority norms"—is not a very potent remedy. Rather, studies should be commissioned to upgrade the tests to remove the bias and increase the accuracy. As community Superintendent Annette P. Goldman said, "We insist upon one test for all children." Every child deserves an equal right to learn. And every child deserves an equal right to a life of as much privacy as she or he can obtain. Test results, no matter how unbiased and competently given, are merely an indication of potential and should remain as such. Not as a lifelong millstone hanging around a person's neck because some computer with a long, long memory keeps the results of that test score tattooed on a child's future like a modern scarlet letter.

As part of this concerted attack on privacy, the Department of Health, Education, and Welfare joined the fray in the fall of 1973. HEW developed a questionnaire aimed at ascertaining the racial attitudes of fourth and fifth-graders. Question: Is it racist to ask children questions like "Do you think black students in your school cause more trouble than other kinds of students?"

Some officials thought so. The project was scrapped. The questionnaire was to have gone to 176 schools in twenty-five states to be completed by 27,000 children, including 1,500 in New York City. The same questionnaire would show up again in the spring, according to a spokesman, and be given to the same pupils, "to measure the effectiveness of Federal funds granted to the schools to foster better race relations."

New York school officials charged that some of the twenty-three questions were racist because they seemed to focus on "children of other races as sources of trouble" and "polarizing" since they could conceivably provoke ethnic conflict. Officials noted that making cooperation with the questionnaire a condition of receiving federal grants was also totally unacceptable. Arm-twisting is rarely appreciated these days.

HEW really didn't have much of a choice in withdrawing their plan, but they took surprisingly little time to lick their wounds before attempting another frontal assault. Three months after their defeat, they unveiled a new questionnaire which they wanted to distribute to 100,000 schoolchildren in April. Adding a new twist to everyone's arm, they also announced plans to set up a com-puterized data bank to include educational, ethnic, and family information about the pupils. The young students at the 227 selected public schools throughout the country were not, of course, questioned about their feelings in the matter. Their inno-cent cooperation was assumed.

Only New York City again stood in the way. Forced by Dr. Lachman's uncompromising stand, HEW agreed to accept the information anonymously; they had originally intended to identify it by name or code number.

"The New York City episode on accumulating a data bank on city children for a Federal study," said Dr. Carl L. Marburger, senior associate of the National Committee for Citizens in Educa-tion, "exemplifies the extreme dangers to privacy which may occur at any time."

At this writing, Lachman was still unsure about the Board's final decision, whether they would consider the meager conces-sions from HEW enough, demand more, or reject the idea com-pletely. A number of groups were pressuring for them to do the latter. Even anonymous information, they argued, could become damaging in the hands of a government with little inherent regard for the privacy of schoolchildren too young to resist the candy of the information-gatherers.

And not only does a child deserve an equal right to learn regardless of race, creed, or national origin: a child also deserves equal protection under the law, it says here. Of course, that theory is a little shaky, too.

In 1967, the President's Commission on Law Enforcement released a far-reaching series of reports on crime in America, a comprehensive study that is still considered the definitive finding in this area. According to the commission, 58 percent of white urban males will be arrested at least once during their lifetimes; over 90 percent of non-white urban males, 50 percent of American males overall, and 12 percent of all females face a similar fate at some time. Yet of those arrested in 1971 for crimes (excluding traffic violations) nearly 4 million—almost 50 percent of the total—were never convicted. The American judicial system, as we all know, is based upon the premise that a person is "innocent until proven guilty," yet one needn't be convicted of any crime today to suffer consequences nearly as serious. For one thing the arrest itself—conviction be damned—is enough to prove a man guilty in the eyes of many people.

Following a couple of widely publicized arrests of school personnel in New York for various crimes, the Board of Education promised immediate steps to keep closer watch on teachers in trouble with the law. Unfortunately, this promise simply translates into more recordkeeping and "improved communications with police to be better informed on teacher *arrests*." (italics added)

When a junior high school general-science teacher was arrested on charges of murdering a Harlem drug-pusher in August 1973, the New York school board reiterated its arrest policy in a circular sent to all school districts. The policy essentially entails the removal from classrooms of teachers *arrested* on drug and sex charges—not convicted, just arrested. The teacher's supervisor makes the decision of whether to remove the teacher following a personal interview to determine the seriousness of the charges and the probable impact on the teacher's students. The board is also printing up new forms in order to keep better records on teacher arrests. "If we get notice of an arrest," explained Dr. Dennis Hayes, deputy director of the office of personnel, "we will send the information to the community district involved with instructions that they are to take appropriate steps and send us follow-up information. That way we have an ongoing file and the local district will have one for their own purposes.''

No complete records of teacher arrests and convictions currently exist on any level of the school administration. But they will soon—arrest records, anyway.

Teachers are certainly not the only ones who have to suffer from the ''arrested, therefore guilty'' syndrome. It happens more often than we like to admit. Perhaps the case that has been more effective in bringing the problem to national attention than any other is that of *Menard* v. *Mitchell*, which began in 1970.

Dale Menard, a former Marine, was quietly sitting on a park bench in Los Angeles, minding his own business. Unfortunately his park bench just happened to be located in a neighborhood where police received reports of a prowler. Menard was spotted and routinely arrested by the Los Angeles police for ''suspicion of burglary.'' Since he was innocent, he was routinely released and the case against him quickly dismissed.

The record of his arrest, however, remained on file and was —again routinely—forwarded to the FBI's national computer. Mr. Menard didn't relish the thought of future employers getting this arrest record just because they put in a request to the FBI for a check on him, so with the help of the American Civil Liberties Union, he attempted to have it removed from his record. He enjoined the FBI from reporting it to anyone who inquired, such as those prospective employers, credit companies, insurance agencies, and the like. The case went through four hearings—two in Federal District Courts and two in the United States Court of Appeals in the District of Columbia in slightly more than five years. It was finally resolved. (Menard won his case—in a way. The FBI kept his prints but in a non-criminal file.)

As the case began to show, through testimony at the various hearings, the FBI has become adept at collecting and disseminating arrest records, but shows little interest in including the dispositions of the cases in the courts. Police officials regularly admit that although it is routine procedure to forward local arrest records to the Bureau's computer data, there is no routine procedure to forward the follow-up reports as well.

In the Menard case, Raymond Twohig, a volunteer lawyer for the National Capital Area Civil Liberties Union, questioned the special agent in charge of the Bureau's Identification Division, Beverly Ponder:

> TWOHIG: Does the FBI make any effort to obtain final dispositions where requests are received for arrest records before disseminating those arrest records?
> PONDER: We urge the contributors [to the FBI's fingerprint files] to submit to us final dispositions, but we don't go out and try to pick them up.

Ponder also testified that no FBI statistics exist to pinpoint the number of final dispositions recorded in the files and that he couldn't make an educated estimate of them.

Many of the police officials we spoke with contradicted Ponder's half-hearted attempt to sidestep the question. According to these sources, they have never been requested to submit dispositions, the dispositions have never been submitted, and if suddenly instructed to begin, they wouldn't know how to submit them. No follow-up forms exist to augment the arrest files with the results of the courts' decisions. A couple of officers, evidently right in line with the FBI position, answered simply ''Why?'' when asked about submitting final dispositions.

The FBI does little to ensure that its arrest records, incomplete as they are, are properly used, once released, for ''legitimate business interests.'' Special Agent Ponder, questioned on this point again seemed to sidestep the basic issue:

> Q: Is there any procedure whereby the FBI or any

division of the FBI inquires into the uses to which the arrest information is put by contributing agencies?

A: No.

Q: Are any restrictions imposed by the FBI on the use to which that information is put?

A: Yes. Official business only.

Q: Are there memoranda or orders indicating that there is a restriction?

A: It is right on the record itself.

Q: Are there any form letters that are sent to contributing agencies explaining what "official business only" means?

A: Well, in years gone by we have brought this to the attention of contributors, that this information is disseminated strictly for official business only.

He supplied the court with the most recent FBI notice to participating agencies, an October 18, 1965 memorandum from J. Edgar Hoover. Ponder testified on December 17, 1970. The only penalty mentioned in the memo for improper use of the records was the cancellation of the service. This is about as effective as the telephone company's power to remove their equipment if it is used to illegally record calls without a beep every fifteen seconds to notify the caller that the conversation is being monitored and recorded. Would they really have considered removing all of the telephone equipment from the White House because President Nixon admitted recording incoming telephone calls without the beep? Would they really cancel the FBI's service to a large police department if a record they provided the department was misused? And miss all of that incoming information for their data banks?

Not surprisingly, the current list of law-enforcement agencies whose rights to the service have been rescinded is composed of only two names: the Police Department of Cabazon, California, and the Sheriff's Office, Northumberland County, Sunbury, Pennsylvania. Only four other local police departments or sheriff's offices have been members of this exclusive club at any time during the last ten years. No other governmental agencies except for these six law-enforcement agencies have ever appeared on the list. It is also surprising that no private institution has ever had its rights to FBI arrest records revoked. Perhaps, as one agent has suggested, no one has been able to determine what constitutes a bank's "official use only" of the records it receives. For example Special Agent Ponder testified that no special instructions were ever sent to banks to help clarify the meaning of "official use only" in this context.

The FBI has never really been very interested, it seems, in tracing its records after dissemination, or in investigating complaints of abuse. Another exchange from Ponder's testimony in the Menard case is a clear example of the naive attitude the Bureau prefers to assume:

> QUESTION: Sir, in 1968 it was brought out that the D.C. Police Department maintained a list of fifty companies to which arrest record information was dispersed by the D.C. Police Department. Did the FBI ever investigate whether that list included dissemination by the D.C. Police Department of FBI arrest records?
> PONDER: We didn't make an investigation but we know as a matter of course that it did not include FBI records.

Somehow, we are supposed to assume that, without any investigation, the FBI was absolutely confident that if the D.C. Police Department *was* giving these fifty companies arrest records, they made sure they separated the FBI files from the rest of the information before they gave it out. If you're one for blind belief, you belong with the FBI.

Even juvenile records, supposedly confidential under most states' laws, are treated with little care. The Bureau simply disregards these laws completely, disseminating juvenile arrest records the same as if they were those of adults.

In June 1971 Federal District Judge Gerhard Gesell ordered the Bureau to stop releasing arrest records to anyone except law-enforcement agencies. In his controversial decision which upheld Dale Menard's case, the court found that "Congress never intended to or did in fact authorize dissemination of arrest records to any state or local agency for purposes of employment or licensing checks." The distribution system for arrest records, Judge Gesell concluded, "is out of effective control."

Congress acted quickly to overturn the order, as Senators Alan Bible and Howard Cannon introduced legislation to enable "any non-law enforcement official or agency" to receive FBI arrest records if state or local laws authorized them to. The senators were particularly concerned, they said, about keeping individuals with criminal histories out of Nevada's casinos and thus completely away from its major money-producing industry. Gambling was evidently more important to these gentlemen than the protection of innocent citizens who have never been convicted of any crime, yet must suffer a stigma nonetheless.

L. Patrick Gray III, former acting director of the FBI, in response to a question from Senator Charles Mathias, Jr., of the Senate Judiciary Committee, tried to make a case for the Bureau's continuing in its role as chief keeper and disseminator of the records:

"The arrest record files of the FBI Identification Division as well as those of many state and local identification bureaus are replete with lengthy arrest records of longtime hoodlums and members of organized crime whose arrests never resulted in convictions. Many sex offenders of children are not prosecuted because parents of the victim do not want to subject the child to the traumatic experience of testifying. Others are not tried because key evidence has been suppressed or witnesses are, or have been, made unavailable. The latter situation is not uncommon in organized crime cases. To prohibit dissemination of such arrest records would be a disservice to the public upon whom they [persons with arrest records] might prey again.''

Gray speculated about "the potential school teacher with two prior rape arrests and no convictions" or "a police applicant with a prior Peeping Tom arrest and no conviction."

Yet this is a complete reversal of the U.S. Constitution, presuming guilt rather than innocence. Gray's scare tactics, raising the specter of organized crime, have nothing to do with the basic issue. His proposal is to convict someone outside the courts merely because he has been arrested, equating any arrest with an automatic verdict of guilty. The millions who are arrested each year but never convicted might as well be hardened criminals instead of innocent people, for Gray would assume them to be guilty without reference to a judge and jury's decision. The FBI, protecting the nation from sexually perverted teachers and police applicants, would set itself up as Lord High Judge and Executioner. The flagrant abuse of due process of law, a cornerstone of our democracy, would, if so easily enacted, mark the beginning of the end of the United States.

Congressional civil libertarians are fighting to prohibit the FBI from disseminating any arrest records which do not result in convictions. Courts are also beginning to question this practice with relation to laws prohibiting racial discrimination. The New York City Commission on Human Rights has taken the lead in this fight, stating in a January 4, 1973, policy report that "it will be considered an unlawful discriminatory practice for employers or employment agencies to ask of any applicant or employee any questions relating to arrest records." Illinois went a step further when it passed legislation which prohibits an employer from denying an applicant a job solely because of an arrest record.

The first court test of this interpretation of the standard employer practice of perusing prospective employees' arrest records was

Gregory v. *Litton Systems,* brought by the American Civil Liberties Union of Southern California. Litton's remarks clearly explained the employer's point of view, contending that the "business justification for considering a person's arrest record in determining whether or not to hire him is the same as considering a record of conviction. . . . It is not a fact, and it cannot be assumed, that all arrests which did not result in conviction are unfounded." Checking applicants' arrest records, they continued, "is one of the most common employment practices known to man. Almost anyone who has ever applied for a job has answered this type of question. . . . The employer who does not obtain and utilize arrest information in determining whether or not to hire is the exception, not the rule."

Yet other testimony at the trial revealed some interesting facts. According to Dr. Ronald Christensen, an author of the Report of the President's Law Enforcement Commission, a man who is once arrested tends to accumulate additional arrests. Many of these additional arrests fall into the "on suspicion of" or "investigative arrest" categories. The detective in television police dramas, at least once an episode, instructs his staff to "haul in the usual suspects." The majority of "the usual suspects" are innocent of any charges; in fact, a study of 1964 "investigative arrests" in Baltimore found that 98 percent of those arrested were released without having any proceedings instituted.

Clearly, a number of important steps have been taken to correct a situation which clearly affects a vast number of our nation's population. Just as clearly, however, any action to control the use and distribution of arrest records must contend with the long history of misuse and virtually unlimited distribution of those records, which in the past have been so widely circulated as to severely blunt the impact of the new judicial and legislative reform. Yet waiting will certainly only compound the crime. The FBI doesn't seem to want to take the initiative to police itself, and will act, apparently, only if forced to do so by a public outcry coupled with even more active legislative safeguards.

Two recent developments which should cause rejoicing in parts of California would be excellent forerunners of a national pattern. The city council of Berkeley unanimously passed a first-of-its-kind directive enabling citizens to see their own arrest records. Coupled with this new "open file" approach, surrounding Alameda County is constructing a new countywide computer filing system. This would normally not be cause for a pat on the back. But what is unique about this system is that it has been constructed specifically to protect individual rights, not to destroy them. Rather than being merely a storehouse for arrest records, it will follow the whole trail of arraignment, hearings, trials, sentencing, prison terms, and parole within any of the county's jurisdictions, thereby, for once, giving a complete and accurate report of an individual's "criminal" history.

California's Attorney General has gone even further, issuing the directive to cut all state criminal records by 50 percent. The plan calls for removing the records, immediately after detention of all persons arrested for public drunkenness and minor traffic offenses, five years after a misdemeanor arrest which didn't result in a conviction and seven and a half years after certain felony arrests.

In all fairness to the FBI we must admit that the Bureau did recently announce its own program to pare down its massive file-system. All of the inactive arrest records of persons eighty years or older have been removed and destroyed by the Bureau's Identification Division.

The FBI seems to feel that we should be grateful for such crumbs. "At least," one agent seriously informed us, "we're not as bad as Nasser's secret police were." He was referring to a recent report from Cairo. According to *Al Akhbar,* at the height of Nasser's reign a three-year-old boy was arrested to secure his reluctant father's surrender. When the father submitted, the child was released. Two years later, Nasser ordered all persons with arrest records re-arrested. The child, then five, was summarily incarcerated for four years.

We can't produce an FBI scare story to match. Not only do we not want to, we don't need to. The FBI's overkill system of surveillance and record-keeping—although not nearly so cruel—is almost as cold and threatening. Most of us under eighty are still on file, or files, somewhere without knowing it.

Is there any way to beat the game? It isn't easy. The system that follows a person from birth to death is a free-flowing, self-perpetuating mechanism that feeds on itself to maintain momentum. Few safeguards are legislated and fewer are enforced.

Banks casually furnish government agents with records of depositors whenever requested. Rarely do they bother to inform the individual involved. After all, they don't have to. But under the Foreign Bank Secrecy Act, the government can require every FDIC-insured institution to maintain copies of each check you write for up to six years. There is no protective machinery set up by the act to regulate the bank's or the government's use or abuse of these reproductions.

The 1970 Bank Secrecy Act was designed to curb illegal use of secret foreign bank accounts and to make it more difficult to commit white-collar crimes such as embezzling and tax evasion. However, the act also allowed all bank accounts to be examined, which they were, by Justice and Treasury Department officials whenever they saw fit.

Now legislation has been introduced to amend the act, and at least require a subpoena for the look and a notification to the account-holder that his account was looked at. Treasury and Justice Department officials vigorously opposed the additional restrictions, of course, with assistant Treasury Secretary Eugene T. Rossides stating that it would be "cumbersome" to obtain a subpoena in many cases, because agents rarely could show a probable cause for inspection.

Speaking of the Treasury Department, its supposedly sacrosanct records are not really so, it seems. And what was, up to now, unofficial and legally unsanctioned—the passing of IRS records from department to department—is in the process of becoming legitimate. A recent executive order grants Department of Agriculture statisticians access to individual tax returns of farmers, supposedly to compile statistics on farm income, distribution, etc. As necessary as those statistics might be, the order sets a dangerous precedent. A staff member of the House Committee on Foreign Operations and Government Information suspects businessmen's returns will be the next open to scrutiny, and then the professionals', and then the wage-earners', etc.

It is not very surprising, when you think about it, that you leave a trail behind you with almost everything you do, but it is a little surprising and disheartening that the trail is so easy to follow.

In checking out a tip which came into a narcotics division from an anonymous informant, a narcotics agent described the procedure whereby he initiated the investigation as to the authenticity of the tip:

"What we attempt to do as far as a background investigation is, we check with the telephone company, we check with the post office, gas and electric companies, different organizations like that. . . . We'd call the Bureau of Motor Vehicles to find out if the John Smith [person investigated] has a car. Then through his operator's license we find out his date of birth and sometimes his past addresses. Then say, in one past address he might have lived for a year in Philadelphia. He might have lived for two years in Fort Lauderdale, he might have lived for one year in Berkeley.

"Well, now we know to contact these departments to request a possible record on John Smith. With the date of birth, it's a lot easier.

"Then we attempt to get his social security number, which is sometimes a little difficult, but if we get that . . ."

This is all because an informer phoned in a tip that something was just not quite right with John Smith, and innocent or guilty, John Smith is being run through the identifying machine —without, of course, his knowing it. The trail he left behind will eventually lead right up to his door, and the course of his future may depend on just what that trail was.

Chapter Six:

The Informers: Friends, Neighbors, Yourself

"We know everything about the people who are going to cause problems in our city. . . . No police department could be successful without the information we glean from . . . our intelligence squad. We know, generally, who's going to do what before they do it. . . . We know who comes into town. We know who's going to leave it. And when they're going to leave it."—Frank Rizzo, Mayor of Philadelphia

"Thou shalt not bear false witness against thy neighbor."—The Bible

A draftee we know was inducted into the Army at Fort Dix, New Jersey. During his basic training, he was approached and extended an invitation to spend the duration of his Army career in the services of the CIC. He had no idea what the CIC might be. When he did ask the one other CIC-directed soldier in his basic training group who the CIC might be, the soldier just looked at him suspiciously and walked away. He, the draftee whom we will call John, was later to learn that the CIC stood for Counter Intelligence Corps, at that time the name of the Army's intelligence branch. (The name has since been changed.)

"What would I have to do?" the draftee finally asked the man who was to give him some tests.

"Well," the recruiter answered, "you won't have to wear a uniform, stand guard duty, or pull KP."

"Wow," said John, "I can dig that."

John had to take a battery of tests, including personality and intelligence tests, and give detailed information about his past life, all of which he did willingly. He also had to write an essay—this was in the early sixties—about why Red China should or should not be seated in the United Nations. Then he was sent back to finish his basic training before being transferred to the Army Intelligence school at Fort Holabird, Maryland.

Little did John know that the CIC was not only doing a routine check on the validity of the background information he had volunteered, but was also doing a detailed "investigation" of him. Family and friends were contacted. Questions concerning all aspects of John's past life were asked. In almost every case, John was later to learn the questions were answered willingly and freely. There was no qualm about telling the stranger with the CIC identity badge everything they knew about John. Even though most of the informants didn't know what the CIC stood for, and didn't ask. Some of them mistook the identification badge for Central Intelligence Agency (CIA) credentials.

Most of the information given—as far as John knows—was truthful and aboveboard, but there was at least one narrow escape for him. The CIC agent sent to his hometown approached the local postmistress, who had known John all his life. She was momentarily confused and mistook John for someone else with a similar name. "Oh," she said, "you mean him. I believe he was just released from jail a couple of weeks ago."

The town was so small that it was relatively easy for the agent to discover that the postmistress's word was not exactly reliable, and the report was—presumably—amended immediately and did not go into John's record.

Because John had been living in New York City for several

years prior to his induction, he was traced there also. Former acquaintances were interviewed. "Was John a Communist?"

"Oh, no," came one reply, "I wouldn't exactly call him a Communist. I guess you would call him a freethinker, though." It all went into the record.

What else was in John's final report? John doesn't know. He wasn't allowed to read it. It's secret information. Especially from John. Information easily obtained from friends, family, acquaintances, and employers—true or false, fact or fancy.

Were these people informers? Yes, really they were, in the broadest sense of the word. We are all guilty of being informers once in a while. We tell things we shouldn't without thinking about what we are doing. Sometimes we tell these things to total strangers for no good reason.

"Basically you have to sell people on telling you things they have no reason to tell you," one investigating agent remarked. That isn't as difficult as you might think. Most people like to talk about other people they know.

Insurance companies know this, so when a policy is taken out by a new potential insuree, and a thorough background investigation is initiated, who is approached to fill in the missing blanks in the applicant's background? Friends, neighbors, and family, of course.

Often an applicant's policy is approved or disapproved depending on what his neighbors think or feel about him, what they know, and what they say. The investigations can be performed by agents of the insurance company itself, or they can be farmed out to private bureaus. Most of the background investigations today are farmed out. New York State alone has approximately 1,250 independent firms that handle such investigations for the companies.

You might think, logically, that it really doesn't matter who does the investigating. That the investigation—if fairly done—is necessary, proper, and—as one insurance company executive remarked—"the only people who'll resent investigations are the poor risks."

But even if all that is true, it does definitely matter who does the investigating and the words "if fairly done" make a great deal of difference. "We're in business to find bad risks," one West Coast manager of an independent investigating agency told his investigators, "if everybody comes out clean, we don't justify our existence." So there is pressure on the independents to slant their reports unfavorably, according to this manager. What may be in actuality unfounded gossip from an unfriendly or just imaginative neighbor may become, in the investigator's report, a fact. We all know people who innocently exaggerate things a little when repeating them, so the man next door who drinks one drink before dinner every night could become—in the eyes of a teetotaling, imaginative neighbor—a regular lush.

"He drinks too much. He beats his wife. He drives recklessly." True or false? The investigator decides.

Of course, insurance companies are by no means alone in the use of informers for their background checks. Credit bureaus use them, too.

In highly populated areas, there are a number of ways of finding out what kind of a credit risk a man is. Usually data stored in computer banks are used, as was discussed previously. But in rural and less densely populated urban areas, a credit bureau may use a local resident as a part-time agent to fill out a questionnaire on the applicant's background and potential risk.

A local merchant in a midwestern state remarked that he often filled out such questionnaires for credit companies. He received so much per application completed. How did he go about checking on the applicant's background?

"If they don't have credit with me, and I don't know them that well, I ask around. Somebody I know usually knows them, and I fill it in that way. I'm usually pretty lenient with them. Unless they're really bad at paying their bills, I give them a pretty good report."

Is the merchant an informer? Or is he just doing a job for money? A part-time credit investigator?

Nobody really likes informers. We tend to think of them as disloyal, sleazy little people who betray confidences for favors or money. We have a variety of labels for an informer—stool pigeon, narc, gossip, spy, turncoat—all with a distasteful connotation.

The police call them "informants" and whether they be a stool pigeon or concerned citizen, they welcome them all, for without their services, they could not exist.

We all admit information about crimes should be reported to the police, but most of us are reluctant to be the one to tell, unless of course, the magnitude of the crime demands it; we prefer to mind our own business. What are the bounds of personal privacy and when does the informer overstep these bounds?

Alan Westin, author of *Privacy and Freedom*, described privacy this way: "The claim of individuals, groups, or institutions to determine for themselves when, how and to what extent information about them is communicated to others."

That's a pretty extreme definition and one which we believe to be totally unworkable. What would happen in an accident case? The witness couldn't give out information on the cause of the accident if the one who caused the accident decided he wanted no information about himself communicated to others. Any trial would be a farce.

If privacy cannot be described so sweepingly, how can it be defined? It all depends on where you're standing. If you're standing over here with us, privacy is a special thing, not to be abused by slander, half-truth, or unnecessary invasion. But it is not to be confused with total, absolute control over one's existence. There are times when there is a need for informants, to use the police term, to help stop crime, to help innocent people, and believe it or not, to help keep us an alive, involved society.

But like everything else, the computers, the recordkeeping, the surveys, the electronic equipment, and the use of informers can be badly abused.

In several cases which have been of national concern, the Federal Bureau of Investigation has badly abused and soiled the image of the informant. The recent trials of the Harrisburg Seven, the Camden Seventeen, and the Gainesville Eight, to mention only a few, brought out some examples of their abuse. These cases relied so heavily on informers who were unreliable, to say the least, that each of the three trials ended in either acquittal or dismissal.

To give you an example of the FBI's overzealous use of an informer, consider the case of Howard Berry Godfrey.

In San Diego, in June 1973, Jerry Lynn Davis, a former Southern California coordinator for the Secret Army Organization—a well-armed outgrowth of another rightwing group, the Minutemen—said that the group was partially financed and organized by an informer for the FBI. Law-enforcement officials and others familiar with the situation have corroborated Davis's account. The Secret Army Organization (SAO) had harassed young leftists in the San Diego area for more than a year with incidents that included a shooting and a bombing.

The group was formed in 1971 to train guerrillas who could organize a resistance movement should the United States be conquered by a foreign power. Howard Berry Godfrey, the FBI informer, was one of the six founding members and contributed the money used to print the group's recruiting literature. Godfrey was considered a firebrand within the SAO and took a "more militant line" than most members. According to his own court testimony, Godfrey was riding in a car on January 6, 1972, when another member of the SAO fired a shot into a house occupied by young leftists. The bullet shattered the elbow of a girl named Paula Tharp. Miss Tharp and other residents of the house were planning demonstrations at the Republican convention.

Godfrey took the gun used in the shooting and gave it to his FBI agent contact, who then hid it under his couch for six months until the SAO member who shot Paula Tharp was finally apprehended by the police. The incident cost the FBI agent his job.

Another illegal act by Godfrey was partially disclosed in June 1972 when a member of the SAO was arrested for blowing up a movie theater that showed pornographic films. The San Diego police learned that the FBI had an informer in the organization and asked the FBI for cooperation in collecting evidence in the bombing incident. At first the FBI refused. But when the police threatened to disclose that lack of cooperation, the FBI relented and agreed to let Godfrey testify against the bomber. On the stand, he admitted that he had supplied the explosives used in the bombing.

Asked why Godfrey had been allowed to operate so long with such a dismal record, the FBI declined further comment other than "We certainly don't condone" illegal acts. Given Godfrey's contributions to the SAO in time and money, Jerry Lynn Davis said, "you might say that the SAO was a federally funded antipoverty program for the right wing."

There seem to have been several "federally funded" or at least federally assisted programs which have an extremely dubious legality about them. Let's look at the three previously mentioned trials: the Harrisburg Seven, the Camden Seventeen, and the Gainesville Eight.

In the Harrisburg Seven trial, the major government witness was a federal prisoner serving as an FBI informer. He said at the trial that the Reverend Philip Berrigan and six others plotted to kidnap Henry Kissinger then a Presidential advisor—and to blow up heating tunnels in Washington and vandalize draft boards across the country. The jury was deadlocked, and the judge decided the defendants should not be tried on these charges.

The jury was deadlocked mainly due to the fact that most of them could not believe Boyd Douglas, a bad-check artist and con man who "befriended" the priest in jail.

In the case of the Camden Seventeen, in which the defendants, including five priests, were accused of raiding a Camden, New Jersey, draft board in August 1971, the judge told the jury it could acquit because of "overreaching participation by the government agents or informers." The chief government witness and informer was Robert Hardy, who testified that the FBI gave him burglar tools and that the plot would have been dropped had it not been for his enthusiasm—spurred on by the government—and his expertise. The defendants were eventually acquitted.

In the trial of the Gainesville Eight, once again the testimony of FBI informers was the key. William W. Lemmer, one of the informers, was also a prime mover in the alleged conspiracy. The star witness was a pudgy, mustachioed would-be Green Beret with a history of mental instability who was once known as one of the more vociferous members of the Vietnam Veterans Against the War (VVAW). (Seven of the defendants were VVAWs and the other was a strong supporter of the group.)

The Gainesville Eight were acquitted of the charges, which had included conspiracy to storm the Republican National Convention with automatic weapons, slingshots, and crossbows. This case, like the other two, was weak, incompetently presented, and based almost entirely on the testimony of informers who were, it seemed obvious, highly unreliable.

The basic unreliability of most informers is recognized by the law-enforcement officials themselves. They are treated accordingly by respectable agents. The following interview with a narcotics agent, still operating in one of the eastern states, not only explains how informers are obtained, but points up the perils of using them.

Q: What can you tell us about the use of informers in your work?
A: Informants. There's a number of ways of getting them. One of the ways that we mostly would get them would be [to get] a person who's arrested. We'd get him to turn. Promise him a little—uh—deal, you know. If he cooperates with you, you'll go to the DA when his case comes up, and he in turn takes you back to his source where he gets the stuff [narcotics].

The other way would be a mercenary informant, who calls . . . who's only interested in the money. He'll give you the information. He'll walk in for buys [purchase of narcotics]. He wants so much money per buy. These are dangerous to use because they're in it for money, so you have the possibility that they'll set somebody up.

In other words, they can come to you and say they saw some stuff in Fred Jones' place. They were just in there. If you'd get a warrant on their say-so, you might go in there and find this guy's never been arrested before. He's never even been involved in the dope scene, but this informant happened to be in his apartment and stuffed some [narcotics] down the cushion of his couch and then leaves. And naturally Fred Jones has no idea that it's there.

Anyway, you take the warrant and you go back to Jones's apartment and find the stuff and you arrest him. He now has a record. The informant's happy because he's getting paid. You're happy because you have an arrest.

This type of informants we try to keep them under very strict control.

Q: What would happen in a case like that? If someone did plant some stuff? Is there any way Fred Jones can protect himself?

A: He *could* request to have a lie detector test taken. But usually when you debrief him—in other words, after he's been arrested and you get to talking to him—you can generally get a feeling of how they're talking and how they're acting whether or not they're really into the scene.

But actually before we take any action on this guy from the beginning, we'd check him out.

Q: You would do a check on Fred Jones's background?

A: Right. Right. Well, we check the informant's background first before anything. We want to know why a person comes to us. In other words, he gives us a call on the phone, he can cut us into something or he comes into the office. Our first question is Why? What's in it for you?

Very few people come in off the streets because they're concerned citizens. Everybody's in it for something.

So this would be the mercenary-type informant.

Other types of informants . . . you get the girlfriend, boyfriend, husband, or wife, who's mad at the other party. So to get even with them they come to us to put them down.

Sometimes this is legitimate. Other times, it's very risky.

We might do a little checking on the informant and we might find out his girlfriend broke up with him to go with the guy he's informing on. Now we see 'the reason.

Q: You get your information other ways . . .

A: Yeah, there's no set way. You might get a call from a telephone installer who was in the house to install a telephone and saw some stuff lying around . . . he would report it to telephone security and then since we work with them, they'll give us a call.

Other times we get information from the local police departments, or the lady next door who lives in an apartment complex. There's wild parties going on at all hours and all this traffic going in and out. She'll call.

Q: Do parents ever give you a call about their son or daughter?

A: Oh, yeah. We'll get a call and a mother's doing the wash and found stuff in the jeans pocket. The daughter's jeans. She'll give us a call and we'll come out and interview the parents. And you have to be careful in this because technically the person should be arrested—the son or daughter.

The parents don't realize this. They call you figuring you wouldn't do anything to my child but find out where my child is getting the stuff. The parents don't want the kid getting involved.

It's the same no matter where you get your informants.

You get them off the streets, you get them in a raid, another department will arrest them, a citizen walks in, a utility man—anybody.

Q: Let's say the lady next door comes to you with some information, as a private citizen. Do you put her name down on your future arrest warrant as an informant?

A: Well, what we do is put it down as concerned citizen who doesn't want to identify herself. That's a way of getting around it to protect her. You're not lying. You're not building something up on the guy she's informing on, but you want to protect the person who's giving you the information and naturally the average citizen who's not fully aware of drugs—just what they see on television—are afraid they'll get into a *French Connection* type situation. These people are afraid that if they find out she gave us the information, they're going to kill her husband, rape her daughter, etc. There's no way this will ever happen. The only time you'll get into a situation like that is if you open up a real big ring. You know they might come back and do something violent like that. It's very seldom.

What we do with our informants, depending on how long they work for us, we relocate them to a place they want to go provided they do the type of informing where they're really giving us information.

Mrs. Lady-next-door, you wouldn't want to relocate her. So we'd put her down as a concerned citizen who called and did not want to identify themselves and we'd list everything she told us and we'd start the investigation from there.

Q: Let's say you get a court case, will her name ever come up in court?

A: No, you go over the case with the DA. Now, they want this to come up. The defense wants this name to come up. What they're going to try to prove is a personal vendetta that this person might have going against the defendant which is the reason they want the name of the original informant.

Now, you can do a number of things. You can go to the lady and say,"Look, there's a possibility your name's going to come up in court. Would you be willing to testify?" She might, and then again she might not. You go to the DA and you request what they call "in chamber." Which is when you and the DA go into the judge's chambers and you tell the judge the whole story on this. Or on the other hand, you can have an argument from the defense because he wants to be present, because he wants to know what the informant's identity is and some judges hold that every piece of evidence against the defendant, the defense has a right to see, to know about.

And if you want to withold the name of the informant under these circumstances, you'd drop charges to protect your informant.

The protection of informants by law officials is not unusual nor difficult to understand, since this is by far the most abundant source of leads to crimes either done or planned. Therefore, the protection of "reliable" informants is usually carried out with great thoroughness. An extreme case of such protection recently came to the attention of the press when Thomas S. Leonhard went to the courts to try and find out what had happened to his three children.

The case went all the way to the Supreme Court, which declined to review a decision that denied government assistance to the father in his efforts to find his children and his divorced wife. The wife had married a former convict who turned informer and was being protected with a new identity, home and occupation.

The controversy involved Pascal Calabrese, who was the star witness in an organized-crime prosecution in the Buffalo area in 1967; his wife, Rochelle, who had married him shortly before and her former husband and the father of their three children, Thomas Leonhard.

Mr. Leonhard sought to compel the Attorney General and lesser Justice Department officials to tell him where they had hidden his wife and children but the High Court, like those below, refused to help him.

Underlying the Government's case was the belief that Calabrese, his wife and children would be in danger of losing their lives if their new collective identities, admittedly arranged by the Justice Department, were to be revealed.

So the informants are protected, and in this particular case the right of the informant to be protected superseded the rights of a father to see his own children. Is this fair? Maybe only a Solomon could answer that question.

It is certain that not all informants are bad, even though the word itself seems to leave a bad taste in one's mouth. Calabrese may have—in turning state's evidence—done more good for the country in its war against organized crime than the anguish suffered by one man over his vanished children could ever compare with.

With still another type of informer—the plant or spy—we begin to get out of the disagreeable side of the whole concept and into the more romantic: the James Bonds and all the rest of those men for hire by governments, companies, and rich individuals. Now, we enter the realms of adventure and excitement. It's one man —admittedly superhuman in fiction—pitting himself against overwhelming odds and winning. In reality, of course, it's not like that at all.

In one instance of narcotics/industrial spying, the same narcotics agent interviewed earlier recounted a time when he was a plant in a factory.

"The person who owned the factory was complaining that the guys weren't working and there was a lot of dealing going on there and the owner wanted them out. So they requested we put an undercover agent in the factory and it was set up with the union and they got us a union card and we went into the factory to work.

"You just work right on with these guys pretending to make friends with them and find out who is doing the dealing."

The work was hard and tedious. The hours were long, and the agent was allowed no contact with his friends during the work week. If, in doing his job, he had to work weekends at the factory, he would work weekends. He didn't even get to keep the money he earned. It wasn't fun, exciting, or adventurous.

"With this type of investigation, you have to watch that the owner of the plant isn't ticked off because the factory isn't producing to its full capacity. But he can't fire the workers because they're in the union. And they can't be laid off, because they're in the union. And they have no legitimate reason to do so anyway. So what they want you to do is come in and clean house for them, because if these workers are caught dealing or caught with drugs, that's a basis for firing. The union can't say anything about it.

"So maybe the guy has one joint or sells about a half-a-bag at five cents [five dollars] a bag of grass or something like that which is generally not that serious. We wouldn't ordinarily bother with it, but it is valid enough to have this worker fired from the job.

"The owner is really not interested in stopping drugs. But you don't know this until you get in there. This is one thing you have to watch out for. They only want you to clean house for them. But on the other hand, you could go in there and find there's a hell of a lot of dealing going on.''

In discussing the unreliability of informers, the draftee who was in the CIC told us that in his experience, the intelligence method of checking informers was so shoddy as to be a complete farce.

One agent in particular had been supplying the CIC with information for approximately six years when John entered the service. Every six months the informer—or agent, as he was called—was given a lie-detector test to check on his trustworthiness, to see whether he had been "compromised" by the "other side." Had he been caught and through money or other persuasion, decided to work for them?

Every six months for six years the agent's veracity checked out perfectly on the lie detector. Then through a change of jobs, the operator of the lie detector for the past few years was removed and a new operator brought in.

In his first test under the new operator, the agent failed the test. Another was performed. He failed again. Through repeated tests and questions, the agent finally confessed that for the past three years he had been working for the other side. The previous operator just hadn't been good enough to catch him in his lies.

In this case, the informer had become an informer on himself —through the (finally) skilled use of the lie detector. Just what is the lie detector anyway? A magic box that—when properly used—is an unremitting foe and implacable breaker of lies? Not exactly, but it is gradually finding its way into the hearts and offices of many nongovermental and non-law-enforcement executives, as a screener of personnel.

Some idea of the scope of this use can be gained by studying the figures of federal use. Recent estimates contend that the tests given by federal agencies are only one tenth of those given by private firms. While no current federal figures are readily available, a study by the House Government Operations Committee discovered that in 1963, nineteen federal agencies gave over twenty thousand lie-detector tests, screening potential employees and for ''security matters.'' Over half of these tests were conducted by the Army. This figure completely excluded the highly classified, and therefore wholly unreported, testing which is done by the top-secret agencies, such as the CIA, known to be heavy users of the polygraph.

Except for intelligence organizations, experts tend to agree that the use of the lie detector or polygraph has probably decreased in government since a decade ago. A 1965 directive from the Civil Service Commission supposedly limits testing to serious cases affecting national security.

But business use is definitely up, way up. A 1972 AFL-CIO study found that between 1950 and 1960, the use of the lie detector in private industry mushroomed between 800 percent and 1,000 percent, and it's been increasing steadily—though less spectacularly—over the last fourteen years. The study said there were more than 300 lie detector firms in operation across the country, doing over $10 million worth of business a year. More and more, employees are subjected to detailed polygraph examinations as an initial condition of employment. Many businesses have instituted periodic testing as well, once every three months or semiannually, to set their minds at rest and maintain a sharp lookout for employee pilferage.

Union reaction to the growing use of the polygraph is strongly anti-testing. Many have instructed their members to refuse to participate in any test under any conditions whatsoever. In a growing number of cases, unions have successfully negotiated contracts prohibiting polygraph testing of employees altogether. This adamant union position, which some employers have caustically charged makes employee theft and pilferage a natural employee fringe benefit, has in most instances forced capitulation from employers, who have been increasingly forced to turn to testing job applicants who don't fall, as yet, under union jurisdiction. A union local, however, recently concluded an agreement with the E. J. Korvette Company that bans even job applicants from being tested. This is very possibly a sign of the future.

In explaining union reaction to such testing, the Executive Council of the A.F.L.-C.I.O. said objections are "not only because their claims to reliability are highly dubious, but because they represent an obvious and blatant invasion of privacy which free men everywhere should condemn if they want to see liberty continue."

Even the International Conference of Police Associations, which does not hesitate to support lie-detector testing of "criminals," had had a standing resolution since 1964 declaring that while a policeman relinquishes many rights to avoid questioning when he pins on a badge, this "does not include compulsory subjugation to interrogation under an apparatus of questionable accuracy, the reliability of which has never been demonstrated in courts."

A recent study prepared by the American Civil Liberties Union on the business uses of the polygraph, known also as the lie detector, notes reasons for its increasing popularity. "One of the quickest and cheapest ways to verify a large amount of information coming from a large number of applicants," the study found, "is to use a lie detector, instead of spending all the time and money necessary to independently check every detail of the applicant's background. The employer can simply ask a series of questions and verify the truthfulness of the responses. The savings become greater and greater as increasing mobility makes it harder and harder to trace an applicant's background." The report, entitled "The Use Of Polygraphs as 'Lie Detectors' in Private Industry," was prepared by two Princeton University doctoral candidates.

The average, everyday lie detector test costs as little as twenty-five dollars, compared with at least one hundred dollars for a routine background check. As a result of this simple economics, polygraph examinations have begun to displace previously standard investigative procedures and have become a routine part of doing business for corporations of all shapes and sizes across the country. Thousands of persons are going to be shocked this year when they seek commercial employment. They will be the ultimate victims of this boom, the ones turned down for jobs for which they qualify because a polygraph examiner has decided that they lied about something or other.

The object of all this controversy is a fairly simple electrical instrument that theoretically measures emotional reactions through recording involuntary physiological changes which occur under stress. The three different physical conditions which the recording pens of the polygraph measure are blood pressure, breathing patterns, and something called galvanic skin response (GSR): the amount of electric resistance in the skin. It seems nobody can really explain why the GSR changes under stress, but it does and is fairly consistent as an indicator of tension. And the polygraph operator watches the three pens scratching their way across a rolling sheet of special graph paper watching for change—for that is what counts—not how high or low the blood pressure is, or how fast or slow you breath, but how much it changes when you lie.

Polygraph experts claim that these recordings can be interpreted by a "skilled" operator to indicate when deception has been attempted. The testing goes something like this:

An individual is readied for testing by being wired up, so that readings of the three indicators can be continuously recorded. A pretest interview, conducted with the machine turned off, either calms the subject or builds tension—depending, examiners maintain, on his innocence or guilt. The actual interview usually begins with a series of simple, obvious questions: "Is your name George?" "Are you married?" and with control questions, "Did you ever steal?" "Have you ever masturbated?" These questions are used to establish a base line on the revolving chart paper to indicate basic nervousness and to indicate the change occurring when the interviewee lies—most people, it seems, lie when asked the two control questions.

The interrogation of job prospects will generally follow the lines of the employer's job application form with perhaps some more sensitive questions thrown in: "Have you ever stolen anything?" "Have you ever thought of stealing anything?" "Have you ever used your employer's money for personal use, even if you replaced it at a later time?"

Those people already employed and being polygraphed, might be asked more specific questions: "Have you been taking money as temporary loans?" "Have you been taking unauthorized discounts on merchandise?" "Are you helping someone else do so?" and so on.

Although a number of examiners insist that routine testing should not go beyond this type of "are you stealing?" examination, most of them agreed that questions about sex are fairly widely and regularly asked. Questions such as "Have you ever done anything you are ashamed of?" while outwardly innocent, are often aimed at sexual indiscretions. The answers often follow the thrust of the examiner, admitting marital problems, past sexual indiscretions, and other items which don't seem to be the business of the employer.

Often, however, explicit questions needn't be asked at all, given most subjects' basic fear of the entire process. How the operation works and what impact it can have on an ordinary individual can be shown by the case of Bill Williams, a fictitious composite of six persons from whose real experiences and polygraph tests this has been fashioned.

Bill is a forty-one-year-old Korean War veteran, married, with three kids. He applied earlier this year for a job with Medium Techtronics, a manufacturer of complex electronic tracking devices and a company that automatically subjects prospective employees to detailed polygraph examinations. Bill was making the switch in companies after eight years with Axel Data Combine, a competing firm, because the new and fast-rising company offered him a substantial raise and increased responsibility. He routinely signed the standard waiver form which declares, "I agree that Medium Techtronics may require me to take a preemployment

polygraph examination and to take such examinations periodically, as the company may require. I understand that my refusal or
failure to take such a test when requested may be grounds for
dismissal.''

Bill had nothing to hide—he thought. The application had asked
if he had ever been tested on the polygraph before and if he had
ever been convicted of any crime, excluding minor traffic offenses. To both of these questions, he answered No.

Twenty-four hours later, after less than two hours with the
polygraph, Bill had lost his chance to change jobs. Confronted
with the machine, he had admitted to cheating on his expense
account; faking expenditures with the help of a friendly hotel and
restaurant and pocketing the difference. Worse than this admission, however, at the hands of an experienced and ever-
understanding examiner, Bill had confessed to a lifetime of
''indiscretion''—a series of youthful homosexual encounters, a
teenage shoplifting spree, a college career sprinkled with political
protests and use of marijuana, and two recent escapades of marital
infidelity.

An unusual turn of events? Not really. The man was simply the
victim of his own fear. After the test results had been cursorily
analyzed, the examiner told Bill that he had shown ''sensitivity''
on a question about taking money from former employers. The
examiner, always helpful and understanding, suggested Bill
''think about'' his answer while he ''consulted a supervisor.''
When the examiner returned, it was to a man who was ready,
conditioned by his own fears and nervousness, to admit anything
to get out of that room. The transformation from prospective
executive to something less than putty in the examiner's hands had
taken less than two hours.

Bill's troubles were not over. Despite the fact that he had just
lost all hope of ever being hired by Medium Techtronics, he still
had his old job, he thought. But not for long. Axel Data Combine
recently contracted with the lie-detecting firm that had supervised
Bill's examination. When Axel Data did a routine search through

the lie-detector firm's files for reports on any of their present employees, the results of Bill's tests were immediately forthcoming, flagged with a "Not Recommended" sticker. Consequently, Bill found himself jobless, and it was unlikely he would find a job in his chosen field without moving across the country . . . and staying away from polygraphs in the future.

Many people, an examiner told us, have a compulsion to confess. So long as they feel the possibility of any uncertainty as to their guilt, they are able to hesitate and hold back. Once the uncertainty is forcibly removed, and that is, after all, the real function of the polygraph, they confess freely, often to such an extent that the examiner has to shut them up. The confession becomes the ultimate vindication of the employer's use of the polygraph, the acid test of its validity. If the machine can guarantee honest employees, as the confession would seem to indicate, the employer is easily sold.

The question of the polygraph's validity is very much a question. The detractors contend that numerous technical studies which assert that the polygraph works are scientifically flawed, but because people believe the flawed tests, their belief results in a self-perpetuating circle of irony: Belief in the polygraph's efficiency results in a high rate of confession, which in turn induces further belief in the machine.

Professor James H. Sholnikoff, writing in the *Yale Law Journal* in 1961, concluded that successful use of the polygraph relied entirely on "the myth of infallibility" for its psychological impact in forcing confessions. A year later, an article in the *Harvard Business Review* declared that "the polygraphic method will be effective only as long as people believe that it is a real 'lie detector' and confess their guilt when confronted with the fancy-looking squiggles on chart paper." Professors Ronald L. Colier, Lawrence A. Gustafson, and Richard A. Sternbach reported the polygraph's accuracy as "close to 70 percent," a far cry from the industry's claim of near-total invincibility. And the fact is, nobody has yet been able to devise a real check on the machine's reliability—and whether the margin of error is less than 1 percent or more than 50 percent, nobody knows.

The use of the lie detector grates on the sensibilities of many who have been the subject of its tracings, including an increasing number of lawyers and legislators who question its right to invade the subject's privacy. The previously cited ACLU study, reacting to the criticism of such "polygraph victims" and the growing legions of its enemies, has called for the total abolition of the device as a personnel tool. It argues that the entire process is "degrading to human dignity," that it completely overturns the democratic notion of "innocent until proven guilty," and that it "forces one into a position of self-incrimination." Any adverse findings, the study declares, abrogates a person's inherent right to confront his accusers. The entire technique is "an illegal search and seizure of the subject's thoughts, attitudes and beliefs" under the Fourth Amendment.

John Evell, vice president for research of the American Management Association, put his finger on the uneasiness engendered over the growing use of the polygraph: "People may feel uncomfortable about going through the process even if they are not crooks, because no one can be sure of what they may reveal in the presence of the machine. Everybody has something tucked away in their background that they are not proud of and wish to leave unexposed."

Various legislators are joining in the fray, led by Senator Sam Ervin, who has branded the lie detector a form of "twentieth-century witchcraft" appropriate for a police state. As chairman of the Senate Constitutional Rights Subcommittee, Ervin has sworn to introduce stringent legislation to entirely ban the polygraph, "one of the most pernicious of all the pseudo-scientific instruments of the twentieth-century soothsayers. . . [and] an unconstitutional means of obtaining the products of man's mind for employment purposes."

So far, only twelve states have statutes restricting the use of any form of lie-detecting devices in personnel work. Unfortunately, the majority of these laws are shot through with exemptions, semantic loopholes, and weak or nonexistent enforcement provisions. Ten states, though not banning the machine, have at least enacted legislation to regulate its practices and license the practitioners. The Equal Employment Opportunity Commission, trying to take up the slack of the legislators, recently filed a suit contending that the polygraph represents a discriminatory labor practice when applied to preemployment screening. At this writing, the suit is still unresolved in the courts.

Certainly the field has unlimited potential for abusive practices, and unless it is legislated out of existence, the polygraph will probably become increasingly popular as a cheap, quick way to check out job applicants.

Another recent scientific development which seems to pose even more problems than the polygraph is the Psychological Stress Evaluator (PSE), which could change forever the relationship each of us has with others, including spouses, political leaders, businessmen, and so on.

Allan D. Bell, president of Dektor Counterintelligence and Security, which markets the device, described how the PSE works: "There are physiological tremors inherent in the muscles of the human body which are going on all the time when the muscles are in use. Under stress, however, the amount of tremor decreases. The muscles of the voicebox exhibit these same tremors, as well as the stress effect. Using the electronic equipment we've devised, you can examine a tape recording of a voice to watch what happens to these tremors. The extent of the tremor is inversely proportional to the amount of psychological stress the person is feeling."

The thing that is far more frightening about the PSE than the polygraph is that this is a long-distance device, for it can use voice recording to detect falsehoods without the cooperation or even the presence of the speaker.

The PSE is already being used in employment interviews, investigations, customs checks, and even psychiatric practice.

Government intelligence agencies have already purchased four of the $3,200 machines (twice as expensive as the polygraph), allegedly only for testing purposes. It has been used in four court cases already, all in Maryland, which ended in dismissal of charges in three instances and conviction in the fourth.

Dektor says that they are selling about 350 of the devices a year, which compares to sales of about 400 polygraphs, and that the machine is highly reliable. But the reliability of the PSE, like its forefather, the lie detector, has not been proven. Experts agree that while it may be able to pinpoint stress like the lie detector, neither can prove that the stress is in any way the result of attempted deception. Nevertheless, Dektor claims to have monitored the "To Tell The Truth" television program, in which two of the contestants are impostors, lying all the way, while the other contestant tells the truth. They claim to have guessed the "true" contestant 94.7 percent of the time. No independent tests have been presented by which to compare the company's claim.

The most serious objection to the new development in lie detection is still ethical. The machine, even Dektor admits, can be used covertly, thus invading the privacy to which even liars are presumably entitled under the Constitution.

Monroe Friedman, a Washington attorney, speaking at a meeting of the American Psychological Association, declared that "if one ideal distinguishes the open society from the totalitarian, it is a recognition that things of the mind and the emotions are inviolably personal."

To add even more momentum to this drive toward total violation of the mind and emotions, a "new" polygraph has been devised—the multichannel polygraph, which, through sophisticated methods undreamt of by old hands at lie detection, relates the ephemeral musings of the mind with physically measurable body reactions.

Instead of the three pens normally tracing their story across the chart, the new polygraph is a ten-thousand-dollar streamlined model with as many as sixteen channels, which record such variables as pupil size, eye movement, muscle tension, brain waves, skin temperature and blood volume in the finger. It is usually hooked up to a computer to measure these new reactions, readings so fine they were all but overlooked by the relatively insensitive machines of the past.

The new achievement, which an eminent Ivy League professor declared "may become to modern psychology what the electron microscope has become to biologists," might rival the microscope in its ability to ferret out previously hidden shadows of nature. Inventive scientisits are already employing the new breakthrough to attempt predictions of political behavior by means of objective psychological signs, to measure a child's "capabilities" before he is even able to speak and in rapidly expanding experiments in biofeedback techniques.

The scientists are quick to point out that the research is really to help man understand himself better, not to control him. It would make us more comfortable and amenable to this explanation if the walls between the two goals were not so paper-thin.

Things have gotten pretty tight when you realize that the informers of old—the friends and neighbors—have been replaced by our own gossipy body functions. Maybe a modern suit of armor will come into fashion. A thin plastic covering which smothers the telltale whispers our body makes.

It just might work. Until some genius invents a device that can analyze the wrinkles we make in the plastic sheath when we are under emotional stress.

Until such a protection is invented, however, our best defense is to refuse to take lie detection tests for employment purposes as vocally and emphatically as possible, to support those unions and other organizations which are fighting the tests, and to impress upon our elected representatives how we feel about these invasions of our privacy.

Chapter Seven:

The Dossier Dictatorship

There is the natural human dislike of becoming a statistic—particularly when the statistics grow into a lengthy dossier providing more or less intimate details about one's daily living habits. Even more particularly when that dossier is secreted within a vast, impersonal electronic information system to which any number of unknown people may have access.—Robert P. Henderson, Vice President and General Manager, Electronic Data Processing Division, Honeywell.

In Orwell's *1984*, in that nightmarish world where "nothing was your own except a few cubic centimeters inside your skull," freedom still flickered within the mind, but dimly. For it existed only at the whim of the Thought Police, who could easily destroy even that sanctuary at will. Physical surveillance was a way of life, and life itself was little more than a programmed routine where beauty died along with freedom or was banned along with hope, love, and dreams. Few men had the courage to remember any Before. Only Now existed, and Tomorrow never came. Man was a manueverable statistic.

And the computers—rows upon rows of vast data banks, ever-whirring tapes, and ever-blinking lights—were there. Each individual's history from the color of his eyes to the results of his last tetanus booster shot were on those tapes, available at the flick of a switch or the push of a button to whoever wanted to know the intimate details of the individual whose file number was 3737-58.

That was fiction. And it still is. But the potential for creating that nightmarish world as a reality is already here and, in all likelihood, there is on some tape, somewhere in some machine, an actual file number 3737-58. And if you looked at the print-out from that computer tape, you'd probably find that his eyes are blue and the results of the last tetanus booster were negative. And that he is suspected of sympathizing with enemies of the duly elected, mandated government.

Unlikely? Hardly. For as Jerome Weisner, president of the Massachusetts Institute of Technology, remarked, "I doubt that anyone is aware of the full extent of surveillance and information collection activities that go on in this country."

In fact, few of us really know very much about computers at all, let alone what is stored in all of these marvelous machines. Our relationship with this ever-increasing mass of advanced electronic brains is generally limited to the monthly bills and bank statements which all too often seem to contain frustrating computer-created or computer-inspired mistakes. For us, these impersonal "do not bend, spindle, or mutilate" entities are simply another mildly bothersome but hardly threatening offshoot of the extensive technological revolution of the last two decades.

At worst, it seems to us, computers add a few more hassles to an already overcomplicated life. They are to be tolerated, though not always gladly.

At best, the new brains, so obviously superior to humans in strictly mechanical functioning, are to be held in a state of studious awe, praised for their sheer speed, prodigious memories, and just plain mind-boggling abilities, such as solving the square root of two and rounding it off to the millionth decimal-point. The computer helps solve traffic problems both on earth and in space, and it does all sorts of good things like that.

According to this view of the computer, we owe it to ourselves to see that it is constantly improved and widely used, because these improvements and wide use will undoubtedly add more affluence to an already affluent society. Computers are in the long run a pretty good deal.

The dog has been displaced—a mass of electronic hardware and software is man's best friend.

For all these hurrahs, the modern miracle—the electronic computer—is potentially the greatest threat to our freedom ever devised. But why? It is, after all, a man-made machine, and for all its speed and efficiency, its tapes would not whir nor its lights blink without a human programmer telling it what to do.

So like man's previous best friend—the dog—the computer is inherently innocent. It is over the human trainer or programmer that we must keep a close watch. It is not threatening to think that the computer is a servant in the hands of man. However, substitute the words big government, credit companies, or the armed forces for the word "man" in that phrase, and the reason for the threat becomes much clearer.

The United States government, the world's largest and most cumbersome bureaucracy, was a primary target for the computer industry. Its many agencies and subagencies were the perfect spots for the computers, and they were soon being routinely purchased to aid in the deciphering, filing, and remembering of the billions of bits of information a government as large as America's accumulates daily.

The first Univac was acquired by the Census Bureau in 1952. Since then, the government has become the industry's largest customer, purchasing nearly one half of the computers produced each year. Many governmental agencies, like their counterparts in the corporate sector, began to switch over to computers in the last decade out of necessity, determined to modernize, no doubt, for the benefit of the public. Somewhere along the line, the public was left behind.

To be more precise, they were left on tape.

With the justification in the mid-sixties that a revolutionary age of assassination, violence, political dissent, and civil disorder required it, the government began collecting instantly retrievable information on "persons of interest." Such a person is the intelligence community's definition of a citizen (who may have no criminal record) of whom the government wants to keep track, hoping to avert subversion, rioting, violence, or harm to the nation's leaders.

The right to privacy is generally the first right to be legislated out of existence in a modern police state. But in the United States the growing rise in dossier-accumulation might soon accomplish the same end without the necessity of any tedious and time-consuming passage of the appropriate legislation.

What is developing from this outwardly reasonable decision of the executive branch to computerize its various departments, therefore, was actually the systematic and deliberate construction of a national data bank.

"The government has a dossier some place, somewhere . . . on just about everyone," said Supreme Court Associate William O. Douglas in a 1966 address at the University of Pennsylvania. Chances are there are more than one in many cases. A survey of the executive branch has disclosed a frightening number of agencies and departments that maintain computerized files on American citizens. Following are some examples:

***The Department of Housing and Urban Development (HUD) has 5.4 million dossiers on individuals who bought homes with loans guaranteed by the Federal Housing Administration.

Officials are now reportedly still considering the integration of FBI computer data on "investigations of housing matters" since 1954; the Department of Justice's Organized Crime and Rackets File, and the Federal Housing Administration Sponsor Identification File, into their Adverse Information File. This would add 325,000 three-by-five index cards to their already-staggering total. At that point, their data bank would contain the information on all persons ineligible to do business with HUD.

***The Bureau of Customs' central automated data-processing intelligence network sends out twenty-four-hour-a-day suspect information to all ports of entry to the United States. According to the Office of the Secretary of the Treasury in 1971, their suspect records only contained a "modest" 3,000 names.

***The National Science Foundation has established a data bank for scientists.

***The Department of State's Passport Office has established a data bank called a "Lookout File" of 243,135 persons—defectors or expatriates wanted on criminal charges, involved in child custody or desertion cases or indebtedness to the government, subversives, AWOL military personnel, and noncitizens, among others.

***The Department of Health, Education, and Welfare recently established a data bank on over 300,000 children of migrant farm workers, to "speed up the distribution of their scholastic records," according to a spokesman. The records, however, will include teacher judgments ("negative attitude," "slow learner," "lazy") and evaluations. There is no statutory control over the dissemination of this data by its local recipients. The innocent children might eventually discover that, merely because they were born to a particular set of parents, prospective employers, curious insurance investigators, or anyone with a "legitimate business reason" will have access to all of the information on file, although a spokesman for the network denied this.

The network containing this information is called the Uniform Migrant Student Record Transfer System, and is operated by the United States Office of Education.

To be sure, there are legitimate reasons for the computer data banks on these pupils. Patrick Hogan, a program specialist for the network, said that state officials involved in migrant education met to discuss common problems in 1969 and "everybody had one great problem. The kids never came with any records. We couldn't be sure how old a child was, what grade he belonged in, what ability levels he had.

"We also didn't know anything about his health record in most cases. Someone told a story about a boy who had been vaccinated seven times for polio because no one knew whether he had had the shots before."

From the Record Transfer System's central computer in Little Rock, Arkansas, there is a total of 137 teletype terminals linked to all of the 48 states in the continental United States.

Mr. Hogan stated that to protect the privacy of the students and their families, only authorized education officials are allowed access to the information. An FBI agent who was hunting for a child's father was once refused information on the family's whereabouts.

***The Department of Transportation's Highway Safety Program has the dossiers of the 3.8 million drivers who have been denied licenses or have had them revoked or suspended in its National Driver Register Service. They plan to install direct access terminals in police headquarters, courts and licensing offices in all fifty states in the near future.

***The Social Security Administration has the earnings records of nine out of every ten job holders on file. The records of 28.9 million senior citizens receiving social security benefits and 21 million citizens on Medicare are also computerized.

If the proposal by New York State Welfare Inspector General George F. Berlinger is adopted, the Social Security Administration will be even more bloated with names and numbers, for he suggested that every baby be given a Social Security number at birth that would be used to keep track of its eligibility if the baby grows up to be a welfare client.

Berlinger's proposal was predictably labeled as "a step toward 1984 and Big Brother government" by Ira Glasser, director of the New York Civil Liberties Union. This "gets to be pretty close to the universal identification system that has always been one of the tools of a totalitarian society," Mr. Glasser went on, and then proceeded to rage at the plan even more.

"It might be efficient from Mr. Berlinger's point of view to have every baby stamped on the heel," he said. "Or maybe he could catch a few more welfare cheats if the government could open our mail or listen to our telephone conversations."

Of course, Mr. Berlinger didn't agree. A spokesman for the state welfare inspector said, "I don't see any danger in the taxpayer knowing a welfare recipient is who he says he is."

Among other aspects of the proposal was the inclusion of "a computerized central data bank which would give statewide clearance and control of applicants and recipients. The data bank would have access to government information on unemployment insurance, motor vehicle registrations, and tax records in verifying information provided by applicants and recipients."

***The Department of Agriculture's computer system holds the records of 1 million borrowers and 60,000 investors who did business with the Farmer's Home Administration and 250,000 farmers who are buying federal crop insurance.

***The Internal Revenue Service's National Computer Center has a master file of 80 million accounts on magnetic tape, available at cost to any state and the District of Columbia.

***The computer within the austere walls of the Pentagon contains the dossiers of 7 million employees who were investigated for either criminal or security reasons. Permanent records, it is anticipated, will be maintained on about 3.5 million of these individuals.

***The Veterans Administration keeps tabs on 15 million veterans and their dependents who receive benefits.

***The Department of Labor increased its files from 2 million to 10 million in the last two years. (All of the agencies have increased their capacity for storage and the dossiers stored, but few in such a dramatic fashion.) Included are those who either have participated or are currently participating in federally funded work or training programs. Their records are coded by social security number.

***The Federal Housing Administration, besides its records of 4.5 million loans, keeps the records of 300,000 builders it has placed in the aforementioned Adverse Information File.

***The Secret Service has the most modern computer currently active in the government. Its Honeywell 2200 system contains information on "about 150,000 persons," two thirds of whom are cranks, criminals, counterfeiters, forgers, etc., and the rest of whom are government employees and press representatives with access to the White House. The government probably sees little irony in placing the two groups together.

The unique feature of the Secret Service system is its "random access capability." This means that the computer can spew out all of the dossiers which match any of the general criteria it is programmed to check. For example, if an agent were interested in a male graduate of Princeton University within the last five years who was also over six feet tall, with blue eyes and blond hair, and currently living within a hundred-mile radius of Los Angeles, he could have at his fingertips, within seconds, a complete read-out of all of the individuals on file who fit that specific description.

According to spokesmen, this capability enables the Service to pinpoint possible troublemakers in a specific area in which the President is traveling. Actually, it adds just another dimension to the already lush overgrowth of the federal computer jungle. According to Assistant Director Thomas J. Kelley, direct automatic teletype access to the computer from all of the local Service bureaus is anticipated in the near future.

***The Civil Service Commission is not computerized as yet. Nevertheless, it keeps 625,000 folders in its "investigative file," 2.1 million index cards on electric-powered rotary cabinets in its "security files," and 10.5 million cards in its "security investigative index," which contains information on all former and present federal employees and employment applicants who have undergone Commission investigations since 1939. With everyone else computerized, can the Civil Service be far behind?

Just to insure that the states are not left to wallow in the manual maze without being privy to the latest electronic wizardry, the Department of Justice has been active in establishing computer data systems in cooperation with the state governments and is funding state programs for law enforcement, civil disturbances, and other surveillance. Ten northeastern states, for example —with the sole exception of that cradle of liberty, Massachusetts—have set up their own regional data-bank system. Push a button, and out spews information on millions of citizens—traffic violations, histories of mental patients, and millions of other statistics.

Oklahoma and New Jersey had even gone as far as independently collecting and computerizing dossiers on political activists within their borders, until the American Civil Liberties Union sued them both.

The result is that this wholesale dossier-gathering—for whatever initial reason—has now become a mass surveillance system.

It is true that access to these computer files is limited, and only those with official clearance and a genuine need to know are supposed to be able to get information from them. But ways around such limitations are so simple and so apparent that there is virtually no protection for those people who are "on file."

In an interview with a narcotics agent concerning surveillance of private citizens, the issue of filing information received from such surveillance came up:

QUESTION: What happens to the transcript of a legal

telephone tap when no adverse information is found on the subject being tapped?

AGENT: They go in his file. This would be for future reference in the event he's ever investigated again. Every name, every phone number is kept in a record. . . . Every time we do an investigation on someone the file is kept even if it's an unfounded investigation. But no one has access to them.

Q: Could the FBI get them?

A: I imagine they could out of a courtesy from our department to their department. In other words, they might have an investigation on someone and give us a call. And we'd say, "Yeah, we had one on them in '72. It was unfounded." So we'd run it down and tell them what we had, information that he was meeting with so and so, but nothing more. Or if we had followed him, we'd keep a list of who he visited and how many cars he was seen in or if a car stopped to see him, we'd take the tag number. We'd give them that.

Q: What is this new interdepartment computer hookup?

A: Here we call it the ———— Network.

Q: Does it go into other states?

A: Yeah. You can go to some city up here and send a message to Alaska. [Teletype]

Q: Could you punch out my name and get information on me?

A: Yeah.

Q: And get it from all over the country?

A: No, they're working on it through the National Narcotics. They haven't got it yet as far as I know. The Customs has one where I can punch out your name, and if you've ever been arrested, it will come back. It will show.

Q: Would Customs give that information to you?

A: Oh, yeah. I'd call; they'd give it to me over the phone.

Q: Would you have to have a legitimate reason to get that information?

A: No, not really. I'd say we're doing an investigation. Again this comes down to your personal contact with the guy. In other words, you'd ask for Joe. Hey, Joe, do me a favor. Run this through. (You're not going to put that in there?)

Q: Let's say someone in your department had it in for someone. A personal vendetta. Can he get all the information he wants on that person just by calling Joe and asking for a favor?

A: Certainly. He can do it, but, today, at the present time, he'd be very dumb.

Q: But the information is available to him?

A: It's available, yeah. You're a law-enforcement officer and you have the right to call the other department and they'd give you the information.

Q: Can you get such things as credit ratings?

A: You can get that information too, I'd call and run a credit check on you. Again, it can be abused if you want to.

Q: It can be abused?

A: Yeah, certainly.

Civil libertarians are understandably concerned. At least, the accumulation of dossiers kept in file folders and on index cards was limited to a great extent by the confines of space and the limits of practical workability. The computer admits to no similar limitation. As far back as 1967, Dr. Alan Westin pointed out that "a 2000-page dossier of everyone in the United States can be stored in a ten by twelve room and be available in five minutes." Rapid advances in methods and mechanics of miniaturization makes even that terrifying estimate out of date—the room has since shrunk.

It seems that every advance in the computer field, while certainly helpful in solving problems and developing new applications for old methods, can just as conceivably be employed in less helpful and more sinister ways. IBM's new electronic switching device, for instance, replaces the transistors that operate the thousands of switches in a large computer. The switches, speaking the "Yes-No" binary language of computer technology, determine the overall speed of the computer. The newly developed invention cuts the previous switching interval one hundred times. This gives computers far greater capacity, enabling them to handle such complicated tasks as a moon mission or a five-day weather forecast for the Weather Bureau. It also cuts the five minutes needed to retrieve your dossier to about three seconds.

The Executive Branch, it seems, is aware of the quickening strides of scientific progress. According to the July 11, 1971, New York *Times*, "The White House is sensitive about the installation of a new high speed IBM computer known as System 370, Model 155. The project has been classified. Officials of the International Business Corporation referred questions about the installation to 'the government.' The General Services Administration, which should know about it, never responded to an inquiry. . . . The computer system is capable of storing 800 million characters of data and printing it out at 2000 lines per minute. It can execute an instruction in 115 billionths of a second. It sells for more than $2 million."

Congress is just as aware of the dangers that such advances produce, but in contrast to the executive branch, they prefer to talk about it. Senator Sam J. Ervin, Jr., has declared, ". . . the undisputed and unlimited possession of the resources to build and operate data banks on individuals and to make dossiers about people with the aid of computers and electronic data systems, is fast securing to the executive branch officials a political power which the authors of the Constitution never meant any one group of men to have over all others. It threatens to unsettle forever the balance of power established by our Federal Constitution.''

Americans are not the only ones concerned about the rapid rise of permanent electronic recordkeepers. Commissions in Canada, Great Britain, and Sweden have voiced objections to proliferating data-collection systems. Sweden enacted legislation to protect its citizens from computer abuses. It's the only country to have done so.

Canada, it seems, would have a lot of trouble doing the same thing anyway, for Americans have greater access to data about Canadians than Canadians themselves. According to a report by federal communications experts, data about birthdates, bank balances, medical histories, credit ratings, arrest records, and other highly personal information about Canadian citizens flows uninhibited through the computer systems of the United States. It was further discovered that many Canadian data banks ''are located wholly or in part outside Canadian borders and therefore outside the reach of Canadian law.'' The report cited a number of specific examples:

American Express maintains the largest credit data bank on Canadians, with over 130,000 credit records on file. The Medical Information Bureau of Boston, a conglomeration of some seven hundred life insurance firms (eighty of which are Canadian) has files on 800,000 Canadians. Nine million persons who have defaulted on debts, 8,500 of them listing Canadian addresses, are on file with the Credit Index in Morristown, New Jersey. Altogether it was estimated that 8 percent of all personal files on Canadians are stored in the United States and most of this data, according to A. E. Gottlieb, Deputy Communications Minister, are ''contributed exclusively or predominately by non-Canadian sources.''

So don't think you can run over the border to our northern neighbor and escape Big Brotherism.

But to get back to our own problems . . . It was estimated in 1969 that there were 180 million dossiers on American citizens in computers throughout the nation. That number has increased in the past four years, undoubtedly, but government being what it is, estimates are hard to come by in this area.

The Federal Bureau of Investigation always seems to be lurking in the shadows of every situation that concerns individual privacy and government information-gathering, and as one might suspect, the gathering struggle between computers and mankind finds the FBI squarely on the side of the computer.

The Bureau's Identification Division, home of the nation's fingerprint records, was organized in 1924 and presently boasts some 3,300 employees and 200 million prints. Allowing for duplication, these prints are estimated to cover 86 million people, only one third of whom are classified in the "criminal file." Nearly 8 million new prints are received each year, but law-enforcement agencies on various state and local levels account for less than one half of this total. The rest are submitted by banks, insurance companies, credit bureaus, prospective government employers, and the like. It is standard procedure, upon receiving a print, to release all data on the person identified to the submitting agency. This is even true in the case of supposedly sacrosanct juvenile records. Although laws insure their confidentiality in almost every state, the FBI does not separate these files from the regular adult records. They are, upon request, disseminated the same as anyone else's. State laws seem to be totally ignored in this area, a practice, as we have seen, that is not exactly unusual procedure for the Bureau. Since 1932, prints and other pertinent data have also been freely exchanged with foreign law-enforcement agencies. Eighty-two countries presently enjoy these privileges.

In October 1973, the FBI formally apologized and agreed to an out-of-court settlement of $1,000 in damages to a former University of Oregon student body president for the unauthorized divulgence of his FBI file to a radio station news director in Oregon. Thomas Ackerman, a bureau agent, passed Ronald Eachus's file to his news director friend at radio station KPNW in 1971. A station employee then gave parts of the file to the university newspaper, *The Daily Emerald,* which published them.

In a letter written to Mr. Eachus by FBI Director Clarence M. Kelley, the following statement was included:

"I assure you that FBI policy does not condone or tolerate the divulgence of any information from its files to unauthorized persons and that appropriate disciplinary action was taken in this matter in that Mr. Ackerman was reprimanded by the FBI and suspended for one month."

The former student, Ronald Eachus, had been an outspoken critic of the Vietnam War. It seemed apparent that the agent and the station news director were trying to quiet Eachus down by the release and publication of parts of his FBI file. However, Charles O. Porter, Eachus's lawyer, stated after the settlement was completed that they "were convinced that it was not part of a plot from Washington."

The National Crime Information Center, organized by the Bureau in 1966, is potentially as dangerous as all the other data banks put together. The master computer is tied into 104 control terminals in all fifty states and Canada and to the sixty-odd FBI field offices as well. An additional forty state and municipal computer systems are tied into the national computer, enabling approximately 4,000 local law enforcement agencies to make inquiries from their own terminals and insert their own data. Arrest records are quickly furnished to the Bureau via this network, although "no-conviction" records are never solicited, and therefore many, many files are incomplete.

According to Kelley, who acknowledged that the FBI's computer system is more efficient at compiling police reports than at checking them, the millions of files are supposed to "aid the officer in making appraisal of what type of person does he have here. . . ." Surely incomplete data can be of little service in this situation.

The Identification Division will soon be completely computerized and a "Computerized Criminal History System" is being developed with state and local law-enforcement personnel.

The meat and potatoes of the Bureau's work are the files which are gathered as a result of their investigations. During 1970, no fewer than 2,567,373 name checks were made and duly added to the 5,958,000 files and 55,739,000 index cards already compiled. These records should be computerized along with the other divisions in the near future.

To add to this massive file of names, the FBI is concerned with the checking of anyone—including the then Vice President designate Gerald Ford— who has anything to do with the government. President Truman's establishment of a loyalty program in 1947 for all federal employees has been successively continued by each executive. More than 17,000,000 people—government employees, contractors, and affiliates—are presently covered through this program. Much of the investigatory work was transferred to the Civil Service Department in 1952, but the FBI keeps its hand in.

The National Agency check, under the aegis of the Defense Department, conducts separate investigations of everyone with access to defense information. They have complete access to the files of the FBI, Civil Service Commission, Immigration Bureau, and all military and intelligence agencies. The records of over 1,000,000 checks a year are on file.

As the *Wall Street Journal* commented in 1966, "We do not suggest that many officials would attempt to abuse the power [of the computer]. Yet the fact is that even as it is, federal agencies have been known to harass individuals or businesses, just as some of them have not been above electronic prying and snooping."

For as many names and assorted bits of background information as are constantly being fed into the vast data banks from actual surreptitious surveillance, there are at least that many more names and bits of information that are supplied easily and willingly by the subjects themselves.

"During our subcommittee hearings in 1969," reports Senator

Ervin, "case after case was documented of the vast programs to coerce citizens into supplying personal information for statistical data banks in the Census Bureau and throughout other federal agencies."

Sitting with a two-foot-thick stack of questionnaires next to him, Ervin discussed the gathering within the federal bureaucracy. Noting the vast variety of facts and figures the government wanted, he ran through some of the questionnaires in the pile: They range from surveys of smoking habits; specific inquiries about the precise details of any travel people undertook in this area for a year; where they stayed, why they traveled and how, and how much they spent; surveys about people involved in shark attacks, how the victims behaved, how they were dressed, and the color of their skin; surveys of the personal life and financial affairs of people in mental hospitals and their guardians; surveys about the number of feet in the beams of your basement and exactly how far windows are from the ground.

"Inquiries about the conduct and finances of hunters.

"Questionnaires to vacationers about their hobbies, their recreational preferences.

"Surveys of the attitudes, the habits of old people; sick people; disabled people; young people out of work.

"And many, many others."

Each of us who has ever filled out a form probably admitted more about his or her own life than he or she would have liked to. The trail we leave behind is long and easy to follow. For the rest of our lives.

The worst aspect of this trail, though, is that much of it is being computerized and, along the way, such information gathering is coming under the benign legality of the government.

The Census Bureau maintains responsibility for publishing the demographic statistics of the United States. In order to accomplish this, the Bureau's millions of forms and thousands of workers plunge into country towns, inner-city ghettos, isolated offshore islands, and anywhere else another statistic could be hiding.

However, if you prefer not to be one of these statistics, there is some dim hope in the fact that they still managed to miss 5 million persons in 1960.

But besides doing their job, about which few citizens would quibble, these public-spirited servants have begun to join the growing ranks of "information please" addicts, who consider it their sworn duty to extract as much information about one's private life, dreams, finances, and activities as possible from the people they talk to.

In 1967, for example, most citizens received the usual Census questionnaire with its typically innocuous questions. In New Haven, Connecticut, however, 120,000 households received, instead of the standard form with 14 questions, an "experimental questionnaire" composed of 188 questions, such as:

> What is your Social Security number?
> What were you doing five years ago—Working? Military service? Attending school? Something else?
> Does your home have a garbage disposal unit? A color television set? A dishwasher?
> Are such items as heat, electricity, air conditioning, and a swimming pool included in the rent you pay?

These questions hardly relate to the publishing of population statistics. Yet the Census Bureau, backed up by Title I, Section 13 of the U.S. Criminal Code, requires responses to each question, at the risk of sixty days in jail and/or a $100 fine.

As Senator Ervin remarked during the subcommittee hearing in 1969, "The power of the government and the force of Federal criminal law should not be used to harass citizens with unnecessary surveys prompted by some officials vague hope that the information might in some way prove helpful."

Many of the questionnaires that the government sends out —unlike the Census questionnaire—can be answered on a purely voluntary basis, but the recipient is never informed. He is left with the incorrect but never-denied inference that the responses are required by law.

And the forms keep coming—thousands of them every year —sent to businesses, clergymen, city-dwellers, country-dwellers, air-conditioner owners, and so on. When a citizen retires these days, he is at once beset with a new round of forms, led by Form #72-S68005 from the Department of Health, Education, and Welfare. He is never informed anywhere on the form that the answers to the following sample questions are entirely voluntary:

Do you feel you could be earning more money, if you wanted to?
1. Yes   2. No   3. Don't know
How much did you earn at (1) your last job and (2) your longest job?
$———per 1. hour   2. week   3. month   4. year
How much income does your wife or husband earn per year?
$———per year.
Are you receiving any of the following kinds of income and how much monthly? Any company or union pension; Social Security; Federal Government employee pension; state or local government employee pension; military retirement pension; veteran's pension or compensation; railroad retirement; workman's compensation; cash for sickness; or temporary disability insurance, welfare or assistance payments; and unemployment compensation?

Are you receiving any of the following kinds of income? Include any income received by your wife or husband and fill in the yearly amount. Interest from savings, notes and bonds; dividends from stocks; net rental income, excluding maintenance cost, utilities, mortgage payments, property taxes, etc.; annuities purchased individually; regular contributions from relatives outside your home; and other income (from occasional work, etc.)

Computer tapes of this information are maintained indefinitely by the Census Bureau, and a copy of the final tapes is also kept indefinitely by the Social Security Administration.

There are other forms just as privacy-invading and also long and tedious to complete. The Agriculture Census Form for 1969, for example, was eleven pages long and was divided into thirty-eight sections. It required answers to a total of over five hundred statistical questions.

Some of this information was undoubtably necessary and worthwhile to collect. However, as a number of witnesses before Ervin's hearings pointed out, few farmers keep statistics in any way similar to the requirements this form assumed. Thus, for many, "guessing" was the only way to complete the form. Guessing is not the most accurate of indicators.

Besides the tedium and time involved, many people are worried about the legally sanctioned inquiries into privileged areas of one's life. As William F. Rickenbacker, chairman of the National Right to Privacy Committee, lamented, "Why, I keep asking myself, is a law abiding citizen unprotected in his home against the irrational and capricious inquisitions of the government when all manner of degraded suspect and parasitical gentry enjoy the express protection of our highest courts?"

When Rickenbacker refused to fill in anything except the census questions (name, address, age, etc.) on the last questionnaire, specifically excluding all of the sociological questions, he was prosecuted by the government. He was convicted and sentenced to a suspended sentence of 60 days in jail. He had to pay, however, the $100 fine. The Supreme Court refused to review the Appeals Court decision. He is one of only two (the other case involved a neighbor of his) people to be prosecuted for failing to respond to a Census questionnaire under Title I, Section 13 of the U.S. Criminal Code.

In order to clarify just what the legal requirements in regard to questionnaires and forms in each state were, Representative Jackson D. Betts, Democrat of Ohio, wrote to the states' Attorney Generals, forty-five of whom responded, asking two important questions:

(a) Is there a statute in your state which requires compliance (under penalty of fine or imprisonment) on the part of individual citizens or businesses to provide information sought through surveys and censuses by state information-gathering agencies?

(b) Does your state have any statutes restricting the information gathering or investigatory authority of state agencies (other than police) which might be considered as requiring certain personal or corporate rights to privacy?

In the answers to his first question, he found that twelve states require citizens to answer specific questionnaires. Colorado, New York, Texas, and North Carolina require answers to the school census and the board of education questionnaire. Georgia answers the school census only. Illinois—agricultural statistics. Massachusetts and Mississippi—population. Ohio—military census. Oklahoma requires answers to Title 2 (Section 35) and Title 2 (Section 11-8)—whatever they may be. Rhode Island—labor and education census. South Dakota—venereal disease census.

In response to the second question, only New Jersey, New York, and West Virginia replied in the affirmative. New Jersey excludes any questions with regard to creed, religion, or political affiliation. New York's civil rights law covers essentially the same ground, and West Virginia, while not citing a specific law or statute, said it relied on "individual agency controls"—better than nothing, but certainly not to be counted on as the sole defense of privacy. The other forty-seven states have no statutes protecting the individual or corporate entity from inquiring bureaucrats.

But as unprotected as the individual is from the official gathering and computerizing of information on private citizens, there is another area where a citizen is absolutely, completely wide open to exploitation: nongovernment computers. Here is an area not covered in any way—either pro or con—by any legislation. Certain company policies relating to dissemination, confidentiality, and security have been enacted. But little more than this unregulated "self-restraint" keeps the private computer-user in check. This is especially true of credit bureaus, as we have discussed in Chapter 5.

An interesting aspect of this nongovernment computer exploitation began a few years ago when a couple of bored Harvard University juniors were toying with money-making ideas. Since both had computer training and were well aware of what the electronic brain could do, their idea eventually coalesced into a new application for the computer. Why, they reasoned, couldn't the computer be used to solve strictly social and mundane problems?

Like college students everywhere, they believed the most social and mundane problem in life was dating. How to meet girls (or boys) if you're shy? Or how to meet someone you really like, that you know was made just for you?

So a computer-dating scheme, dreamt up in a state of poverty, was hatched that afternoon. They were excited, for they were well aware of the vast market that would be in line for their computer services.

The young students who created the first computer-dating service received more pocket money than they had dreamed of—$300,000 in the first nine months alone. Seemingly overnight, legions of lonely collegians sent in their three dollars to Operation Match, as the newly formed corporation was dubbed, and waited breathlessly until the postman delivered their "computer-matched list of dream girls." Science had suddenly become awfully nice.

Success always hatches instant imitators, and soon the countryside was swamped with computerized dating firms, guaranteeing the "scientifically selected mate, matched to your likes, dislikes, hopes, and dreams." Hundreds of thousands of hungry singles applied as the revolution spread off the college campuses and out into the lonely mainstream of society.

In order to take advantage of this unique new service, potential "daters" were required to fill out a long, detailed, and remarkably intimate questionnaire. This personality test, whose answers were fed into the computer, became one of the thousands stored in the memory banks. The computer then scanned the qualifications of every person of the opposite sex in the applicant's geographical area and selected those most closely matched to his views, likes, etc.

In a typical test, anywhere from five to twelve pages or longer, the questions are generally divided into a number of categories: Absolute Factors (age, height, weight); Attitudes (religion, love, sex); Interests (music, sports, philosophy); Physical Appearance (your own and your "dream's"); Personality and Background (views on family, how talkative you are) and General Information (smoking and drinking habits, income).

Any of you who sent in your three bucks in a fit of "mixer weariness" remembers questions like the following:

I hate myself when I:
A Take advantage of a girl
B Lose my temper
C Fight with my parents
D Ignore someone because I don't really like them

What would you do if your girlfriend told you she had

been sleeping with your best friend but now has decided
she loves you? Would you—

A Tell her it's all over between you
B Go punch your best friend in the mouth
C Forgive and forget
D Let her know you've been sleeping around, too
E Encourage her to keep experimenting

Who would you most like to spend an evening with?
A Richard Nixon
B Robert Kennedy
C Raquel Welch
D Art Buchwald
E Jack Anderson

Is premarital sex—
A Permissible only after engagement
B Permissible only with one you love
C Permissible only if the participants are "consenting
adults"
D Permissible anytime, anywhere, with anyone
E Never permissible

I am most proud of my:
A Humility
B Intelligence
C Good looks
D Bright personality
E Forthright attitude
F Inner calm

As this brief selection from an actual 1967 questionnaire indicates, almost every detail of hundreds of thousands of lives has

been immutably programmed into a few dozen computers. Where are the original questionnaires—in some student's locker or Greenwich Village apartment? In a secretary's file cabinet? In someone's home? Where are the tapes of the businesses that have since failed or simply gotten out of this field? Are they still on some forgotten computer, ready to be spewn out at the push of a button?

No one knows. If you, like so many of us, are one of the ones who took advantage of these firms' offers a few years ago (or maybe only yesterday, since many are still going strong), what would you think if the tapes were eventually integrated with the government's intelligence files or indiscriminately given out to prospective employers with a "legitimate business interest" and enough money to quiet moral scruples? With no real safeguards against these possibilities, they cannot be regarded as far-fetched and simply dismissed.

Chapter Eight:

It Grows Worse:
What to Do about It

"The history of technology is the history of the invention of hammers and the subsequent search for heads to bang with them."—Dr. Matthew P. Dumont, Assistant Commissioner, Massachusetts Department of Mental Health, in American Journal of Orthopsychiatry, *July 1973*

Few people think that the American people, newly apprised of the dangers of governmental and private computerization, should henceforth decline to furnish any information whatsoever to any parties, regardless of their purpose. Besides, if they ever tried, a number of people would find themselves faced with jail sentences or fines or both. A number of agencies, as we have seen, have the right to do just that to any individual withholding information which they regard as "necessary and essential." With such great, and constitutional, civil rights consideration given to the numerous rapists, murderers, thieves, etc., that still walk our streets, it seems rather pathetic that an American citizen would be jailed for refusal to answer whether or not he owned a color television set or air conditioner.

As ludicrous as outright refusal to cooperate might appear to some governmental agencies, it certainly wouldn't hurt to stop, even for a few days, the flow of private information into the computer data banks and take stock of just why it is being done and how necessary it all is.

There is, as of now, little in the way of legislative protection for the individual against unwarranted invasion of privacy or dissemination of freely given information to totally unrelated agencies or investigators. Therefore, many people seem most apprehensive of certain aspects of the growing data banks, specifically those systems that

infringe First Amendment rights by prying into formerly protected areas of life, habits, beliefs, and legal activities which shouldn't be any of the government's business

request information that has no relevance to the lawful function of the agency involved

store information indefinitely and therefore intimidate by the simple act of retention

store information with the victim being unaware of its storage and therefore unable to correct inaccuracies

are part of an increasingly larger network of systems

have inadequate or nonexistent provisions to insure fairness and proper use of collected data

trade information freely with other agencies and government departments, thus allowing freely given information to be used in ways never intended in the first place

Past practice within the government bureaucracy has not eased the fear of these specifics. Indeed, the record of the government information collectors has been one of inaccuracy (routinely including gossip and neighborly innuendoes in investigative dossiers) and irresponsibility in controlling the dissemination of supposedly confidential data on file.

There are still almost no curbs against giving out any of this information to anyone with a "legitimate business interest," as we have seen in the last chapter. Data collected for the specific functions of a particular agency can, through the frequent information trading that goes on within the federal bureaucracy, eventually be used in ways totally unrelated to the original purposes for which it was solicited. Significantly, the American Telephone and Telegraph Company reports that its fastest-growing business is currently computer-to-computer—or "core to core"—communication.

Even "high government officials" have not been above leaking significant details from confidential files to the press for admittedly self-serving interests. There are countless instances of FBI files being strategically leaked without regard to the "victim's" rights of confidentiality of personal information. The late J. Edgar Hoover himself quoted from a number of files in his books. Robert Pitofsky, director of the Federal Trade Commission's Bureau of Consumer Protection, recently lamented the leakage of confidential information to militant consumerists and admitted he had no idea who was doing it. The FTC, he noted, was not the only government agency with such a problem.

Jack Anderson, muckraker extraordinaire, would go out of business without the numerous sources within the government who leak secret and confidential information to him. And remember, plugging leaks in the White House was the mission of the infamous plumbers' squad that committed the Watergate break-ins and burglary of Dr. Ellsberg's psychiatrist's office (and who knows what else).

The total lack of effective security against this kind of unwarranted dissemination has elicited little criticism outside of the victims of such leaks, and in fact one wonders, in the face of excessive government secrecy, if the people aren't better off with a few leaks in the official pipeline.

But, in a way, that is different. The workings of the government are the people's business and not vice versa. The increasing "privacy" of the government in the name of national security is one of the major concerns in the dossier dictatorship, for we want to know who has a "right" to our files, and for what purposes the information on us is being used.

In 1970, the Federal Bureau of Investigation was actually embroiled in a winner-take-all battle with state planners over control of a national data bank for criminal records. The dispute pitted the cost-effectiveness arguments of the Bureau against the well-founded fears of the states that such a system would gravely infringe on the people's right to privacy. The states maintained that they should retain policy control over the national data bank as they did over the Justice Department's seven-state experimental program which was funded by the Law Enforcement Assistance Administration. This program was unique because of the completeness of the criminal histories it contained. It included dispositions of court cases and prison experience as well as arrest records. The FBI's system contained only arrest records, which could be released to private corporations, banks, and insurance companies upon request.

When directors of the Justice Department program, who were mediating the case, recommended that an individual ought to be allowed to examine and correct any information to be contained in the expanded system, the FBI balked. The Bureau's response revealed its inherent disregard for the rights of the individual guaranteed by the Constitution. The system, they maintained, should "only be concerned about what the courts have already said" and should not try to anticipate decisions. In other words, stiffer safeguards would not be introduced unless the courts ordered them to do so. The Attorney General—John Mitchell at that time—was notified of the FBI's attitude and was asked for his opinion on the matter.

Once Attorney General Mitchell decided in the Bureau's favor, the states' worst fears were realized. Only Massachusetts, at this writing, has officially pulled out of the FBI's system completely, although the governor of Iowa has written to the Department of Justice objecting to the National Crime Information Center. The state of Pennsylvania also appears to be moving in the same direction.

In Massachusetts, the records of criminal offenders are being converted to computers, just as most other states are doing, but unlike the other states, systems technicians remove the completed records each evening and lock them in a vault. The original hotbed of the battlefield for liberty, Massachusetts has become the first state to refuse to send these records to the national computer. It has refused to supply criminal background information to other federal agencies which—the state contends—have no right to or use for such information. The Massachusetts Human Services Department has declined a $9 million federal grant because acceptance of federal funding requires disclosure of extensive background information on each drug patient. In addition, the state has brought a lawsuit against a ten-state collective computer system to end their own participation in the massive collection program and prevent the collection of the information from their state at all. As Representative Edward Koch has remarked, ''I wish New York were doing as much as Massachusetts in this area. They're really showing the old Pilgrim spirit!''

Some type of stiff legislative protection—either state-by-state or federal—is in order. New uses of the computers—some already a reality, others in the planning stages—highlight the current concern over safeguards.

For example, can computers be made to think? Most of us would say no without any hesitation. Without man the machine can't function; its mechanical output is determined by what its human programmer puts in. But this is no longer true. Research by the Air Force indicates that computers may succeed in eliminating the human programmer entirely. A quiet 1965 announcement said that the Air Force had succeeded in constructing a rudimentary model of a computer capable of learning from its own mistakes.

The development of an artificial nerve cell or artron, which in clusters has a memory and can solve problems, preceded the construction of the new machine. According to an Air Force spokesman, "artrons respond to punishment and reward by learning desired behavior and capitalizing on their own mistakes. They make decisions and actively seek new and better ways of doing a given task. Knock out some of the artron tools for doing that task and it will dream up an altogether different approach for accomplishing the same thing." Further research in this area, combined with continuing development in microelectronics, might eventually result in electronic brains that rival their human counterpart as thinking forces. All of this research has been classified, and we have been unable to discover what new developments have already been forthcoming.

Our own brains, as a matter of fact, are not on altogether safe ground either. Electronic devices called stimoreceivers, which can be surgically implanted in a man's brain, anticipate man-to-computer-to-man communication. This method has already proven itself valuable for use in epileptics, since abnormal electrical activity, such as that announcing an impending seizure, can be picked up by the electrodes, transmitted to a distant computer, and analyzed. By order of the computer, radio signals are emitted, activate the stimoreceiver, and apply electrical stimulation to the appropriate inhibitory area, thus blocking the attack. This device thus establishes direct communication between brain and computer, *circumventing normal sensory organs.*

Automatic learning (or propagandizing) is therefore possible by feeding signals directly into the brain nerve structure without conscious participation of the individual. As medically helpful as this approach might be and might become, one cannot help remembering the unwritten law: Whenever the government has potential power, they will, more often than not, actualize and abuse that power.

If this sounds overly paranoid, the January 1971 issue of *Transactions on Aerospace and Electronic Systems* should give you pause. Engineer Joseph Meyer, allegedly an employee of the National Security Agency, proposed in that issue the attachment of "transponders" to some 20 million American citizens. These miniaturized electronic tracking devices would be monitored by a master computer that not only could implement curfew and territorial restrictions but would immediately detect any tampering with the device by the "host." They would be, according to Meyer's theory, automatically attached to criminals departing from prison as a condition of parole and to arrestees as a condition of bail, with each "subscriber" thereafter identified by his own unique computer code. Constant communication between the transponder and the computer, aided by an extensive national network of transceivers, would enable constant surveillance of the unfortunate individual.

The whole scheme is certainly terrifying enough if used on a purely short-term basis with a few experimental prison inmates, but Meyer wants the devices to be supplied "on a fairly long term basis," forcing the reluctant individual to "acquire long experience in not committing crimes." All of this is merely, according to the article, a method to "constrain criminals and arrestees into behaving like law abiding citizens."

One wonders whose approval such modification procedures seek—such law-abiding citizens or officials as John Mitchell and Richard Nixon?

Meyer estimates the total cost of the system to come to $2 billion per year, and thinks the most "obvious" way to ease the crunch on the taxpayers is to "lease [the transponders] to the subscribers at a low cost, say five dollars per week." Juveniles might have to enter federal work programs "so they can meet the payments."

Meyer's arithmetic also leaves something to be desired. Twenty million subscribers paying $5 per week would generate some $5 billion per year, but he neglects to mention the apparent profit of $3 billion. More research, perhaps?

"By placing the cost of the system onto the criminal population . . . and putting the subscribers back into the economy to earn the cost of their freedom," Meyer enthuses, "a certain poetic justice is achieved." Frankly, we find the whole scheme remarkably unpoetic as well as patently unjust. By the way, if the system is blessed with initial success, Meyer wants it extended to "monitoring aliens and political subgroups."

Besides the Orwellian proposals of Meyer and other "scientists" one must also consider the problems relating to privacy-invasion which are inherent in the computers as machine. Access to computers is not easily safeguarded. According to some experts, it is not even possible to provide any absolute safeguards against unauthorized access. Some computer practices almost beg illegitimate parties to gain access to the data. At a number of major universities, for example, communication between typewriter terminals and a time-sharing computer is routed through the local public-telephone switchboards.

No one, for instance, can make a telephone call in Waltham, Massachusetts, between the hours of five and six o'clock because the Harvard Business School computer is in operation. A few bright students who made some calls during the "forbidden hour" patched themselves into the computer. So much for security.

Yet even the best security cannot always stop a determined "computer criminal." According to a number of security consultants and law-enforcement officials, the well-publicized cases of computer-related crimes are actually only the tip of the iceberg. Many criminals, even if caught, are never prosecuted, due in part to unwanted publicity but also to real confusion over the applicability of the inadequate laws. As one expert has pointed out, another possible deterrent is the "lack of detection capability to prove that the act actually happened" at all.

A corollary of this surprising admission is the primary obstacle to implementing a favorite solution (just erasing the information) to privacy-invading systems. According to this same expert, there is no way, given the current state of the art, to be certain that any record has been thoroughly erased.

Nor is there any way to insure that the computer is doing exactly what you want it to. It can be affected by change in its environment just like humans, but no one will be the wiser if it malfunctions under certain circumstances.

The 1973 summer brownouts and lowered wattages meant trouble for a lot of New York area computers. Most must operate in air-conditioned and humidity-controlled environments—major alterations in electrical supply can result in computer stoppages, malfunctions, and mistakes. According to some experts, large voltage drops are not particularly worrisome, since most machines are built to automatically cut out like a circuit breaker at a predetermined percentage drop (usually around 8 percent) to prevent loss of electronic data, damage to equipment, or misleading output such as incorrect bills. Less severe changes in electrical volume, which would go unnoticed in most circumstances, can still damage computer operations, they asserted. Since there is no way to check if information has been lost, one wonders how anyone can be completely sure that the data is intact.

The computer industry, obviously sensitive to charges of wholesale leakage of confidential information because of inadequate protection, has really furnished few new methods or solutions to remedy the situation. A "data sequester," now in use in many large industrial facilities, encodes the original transmission and decodes it at the destination. The codes, instead of the computer tapes, must then be guarded.

Other suggestions, aimed at eliminating unauthorized access to the computer site itself, rely almost exclusively on exotic applications employing some combination of either voiceprints or fingerprints. Some would say that this is invading the privacy of the workers to ostensibly protect the privacy of others. A dubious solution at best.

Too often we have failed to look ahead at problems technology might accelerate instead of solve. The energy crisis is one such problem area; pollution of our environment is another. Now we must begin to contend with the crisis of privacy-pollution.

In order to combat the burgeoning national data bank system, we could incorporate physical safeguards into system design. Or we could limit those who are allowed to enter or extract information from the system. We could even have the machine check data against a set of preformulated values and automatically reject questionable information. There could be ingenious safeguards used in the delivery of information. The computer could require a password; it could limit access to a certain type of information; it could record each request, so as to pinpoint the guilty party if released information were later misused.

There are numerous other possibilities which could be employed in complex technical security systems; but really determined individuals, unfortunately, could discover ways to circumvent even the most foolproof security system. The search must be elsewhere; more than merely physical safeguards must be considered and employed.

A report recently released by a government advisory committee pinpoints some of the steps essential to the proper protection of American citizens from the misuse and abuse of personal information currently on file in computer systems. After a year-long study, the group concluded that the American public is fast losing controls of these files of their lives and that a new, computer-oriented "Bill of Rights" must be enacted by Congress for the now fully blossomed technological era.

The committee endorsed two sweeping proposals:

(a) Stiff new legislation is necessary to enable people to know what information about them is recorded in data banks, how it's being used, and who's using it. The laws should also give people the right to delete or correct data if it is incomplete, inaccurate, biased, or based on unsubstantiated accusations by third parties.

(b) The ever-expanding use of social security numbers as a lifelong identification should end immediately. The growing surge towards such a "womb-to-tomb universal identifier" could encourage "government agencies and certain types of private organizations to develop dossiers on much of the nation's citizenry."

The study was commissioned early in 1972 by Elliot L. Richardson, then Secretary of Health, Education, and Welfare. The advisory panel of twenty-four educators, lawyers, computer industry executives, and others was charged to study "changes in American society which may result from using computers to keep records about people." The completed 346-page report, entitled *Records, Computers and the Rights of Citizens*, was submitted to Casper Weinberger, Richardson's successor at HEW.

Noting the well-founded worries of individuals about invasion of privacy by data bank systems and the widespread use of social security numbers as an all-purpose means of identification, it stressed the danger of employing the number like "a password or authenticator of identity" when cashing checks, charging purchases, or the like. According to the report, such use is "not necessary, just convenient." It cited as an example one of the committee's own meetings:

> We met on a Saturday in a conference room in a government facility.
>
> Security procedures required us to give names and Social Security numbers from a telephone booth located outside the locked main entrance to a guard who was out of sight inside the building. The guard was earlier furnished with a list of our names and Social Security numbers.
>
> Given the wide dissemination of Social Security numbers, we were impressed by how easily someone could have impersonated any one of us to gain entrance to the building.

To combat the unwarranted uses of social security numbers, the committee suggested that Congress enact legislation to prohibit any promotional or commercial employment of the numbers. The proposed legislation should also prohibit any organization which now records these numbers from disseminating them without the consent of the individual concerned.

The study reported there was a "possible" drift toward a society ruled by the computer and the millions of dossiers it could contain, suggesting that steps be taken to insure that computerization of private data does not run rampant. Yet it dismissed some of the more "paranoid" fears of citizens about their privacy and concluded that the menace of data banks and dossiers, while potentially dangerous, is not as immediately threatening as the numerous examples cited by the report itself would have seemed to imply.

Unfortunately, the credibility gap which has widened into a precipitous gulf under the Nixon Administration, seems to always dictate a "Watch what we say, not what we do" attitude. Two weeks after Secretary Weinberger declared, "I would certainly endorse the basic principles proposed by the Committee as 'safeguard requirements' for automated personal data systems," the Department proceeded to:

—Revoke regulations protecting welfare recipients from information gathering without their consent.

—Propose expanding the information furnished to the Immigration and Naturalization Service from an alien's social security application.

—Announce that it was considering a requirement that anyone receiving benefits from federal funds must have a social security number.

—Withhold $9 million from Massachusetts because of the state's refusal to provide detailed information on drug-users within the state for a national data bank. The decision, which concerned federal drug-treatment funds, was hastily reversed.

—Suggest a national computer bank to register runaway youths.

Richardson, then Attorney General, while joining in the excitement over the report's release, was evidently embarrassed when only three days later he was petitioned by the State of Massachusetts, the ACLU, and others to "terminate the violations of individual constitutional rights" by the National Crime Information Center, operated by the Department of Justice. Richardson also belatedly discovered that his own Department was suing Massachusetts—his home state—to gain access to the state's criminal records.

Richardson tried to calm the critics by announcing he would tighten privacy safeguards within the NCIC program and try to settle the *United States* v. *Massachusetts* suit out of court. No amount of belated and flurried action, however, could lead critics to overlook the administration's contrary actions in the face of its own committee's recommendations.

Representative Edward I. Koch, Democrat of New York, disagrees with the committee's ultimate conclusion, in any case. And he is not afraid to set the record straight. While originally unaware that Richardson had commissioned the federal study in 1972, Congressman Koch commented on its conclusions while introducing his own privacy legislation in the House:

"I was interested in reading a statement in the Secretary's report, to wit: 'The strongest mechanism for safeguards which has been suggested is a centralized, independent Federal agency to regulate the use of all automated personnel data systems. In particular, it has been proposed that such an agency, if authorized to register or license the operation of such systems, could make conformance to specific safeguard requirements a condition of registration.'

"That is exactly the approach taken by my bill. I am sorry to report, however, that there is an inexplicable gap between the Secretary's advisory committee's findings and its recommendations for initiatives to establish safeguards to protect our privacy. Instead of recommending a comprehensive mechanism for implementing its suggested national policy for data collection and computers, the committee proposes only random amendments to existing laws and reliance on court actions. It suggests that we simply '. . . Invoke existing mechanisms to assure that automated personnel data systems are designed, managed and operated with due regard to protection of personal privacy. We intend and recommend that institutions should be held legally responsible for unfair information practice and should be liable for actual and punitive damages to individuals representing themselves or classes of individuals. With such sanctions, institutional managers would have strong incentives to make sure their automated personnel data systems do not violate the privacy of individual data subjects as defined.'

"Clearly the Secretary's advisory committee's proposals are inadequate."

Clearly a national, automated personnel data system which violates "the privacy of individual data subjects as defined," does already exist, and the need for immediate legislation and enforcement of its strict provisions is essential.

Congressman Koch first introduced the federal privacy bill, which would regulate the collection of material gathered by federal agencies, in 1969. The bill, HR 667, presently lists eighty-one cosponsors. On August 1, 1973, he and Representative Alphonzo Bell introduced HR 9786 (the Senate sponsor is Senator Birch Bayh), which would regulate the collection of personal data by any group, federal or private.

HR 667 covers federal data banks; HR 9786 would extend its provisions to all private data banks as well as non-federal government data banks (i.e., state banks). Specifically, these bills would provide that each government agency or department and all private groups which maintain records concerning any individual —including records which may be retrieved by reference to the individual's name—must (a) notify the individual that such a record exists; (b) notify the individual of all transfers of such information; (c) disclose information from such records only with the consent of the individual or when legally required; (d) maintain a record of all persons inspecting such information; and (e) permit the individual to inspect his records, make copies of them and supplement them.

The bill does specifically exclude two areas from these safeguards, the first being records that are required by executive order to be kept secret in the interest of national security. While certain critics have labeled this a glaring loophole, given the Nixon Administration's flagrant use of the magic incantation of "national security," Koch has added some nifty twists to forestall abuse. He explained to the authors:

"There are certain files that should not be revealed because their disclosure would seriously affect the national security. We'll grant that. According to my bill, however, no agency, on its own authority, could determine whether a file fell into this category or not. If it is believed that some files should not be disclosed due to considerations of national security, it would have to make a recommendation to the President that the files be withheld from public scrutiny.

"Only the President would then be empowered to withhold these files. Thereafter, in order to indicate to Congress that he had not abused that power, the President would have to list with the Congress each year the number of files—and the name of the agency—that he has directed be withheld. If there are one hundred or one thousand, people will probably consider it all pretty reasonable, but if he withholds one or two million —dossiers on one or two million Americans—then people are going to have to conclude that either there is something wrong with the President or there is something seriously wrong with the country."

The second exclusion under the bill relates to pending criminal investigations or prosecutions. Under present law, if there is a pending criminal case against you, you can get your file from an agency, subject to court order and under terms set by the court.

This strict supervision of obtaining a file while embroiled in a criminal action would be continued under the proposed Koch legislation. "This," he explains, "is to prevent organized crime figures and their ilk from using the files in their own defense."

As Koch pointed out, "The enactment of the law certainly does not guarantee its execution, enforcement of its provisions or one hundred percent observance of its strictures by the public. But it certainly guarantees more cooperation than no law."

In introducing S 975 (the Senate counterpart of Koch's House bill) to the Senate, Birch Bayh said that it was necessary to "restore confidence in the American citizen's legitimate expectations of privacy. It is now clear beyond peradventure that we urgently need federal legislation in this area. I would hope that legislation would be designed to accomplish two objectives.

"First, we must define more precisely the nature of each individual's right to a sphere of privacy, a sphere in which he can be free from unwanted intrusion. Any such law should put specific limits on those who would gather and use this information. In short, everyone would know the ground rules and could act accordingly.

"Second, a right without an effective remedy is useless. We must provide meaningful tools for enforcing these rights."

Over two years later, in October 1973, Senator Bayh reintroduced a somewhat modified version of his earlier bill. At the same time Koch was likewise resubmitting his legislation to the House.

But as yet, nothing has been done.

The enactment of legislation along the lines of the Koch-Bayh bills is vital, for as the report issued by the Justice Department pointed out, "The threat to individual rights from unrestricted intelligence operations is direct. Leaks occur. Details which should be kept strictly private become public news. Reputations may be destroyed and careers ruined."

Chapter Nine:

The Terror of
"Law and Order"

*"Is there any potential activity, regardless of who is
supported or opposed, which justifies the Army in spying
on an elected representative of the people?"*
—Representative Abner Mikva

At the very time respect for the law is most necessary, it is all too
often least respected. Our own nation's failure to come to grips
with this irony is made radically clearer each day by the unreal
specter of the score of former White House aides who have been
tainted by accusations of bribery, extortion, obstruction of justice,
and shady financial deals.

The history of the United States is premised on the warm
welcome of dissent in the abstract but is nevertheless replete with
strict punishments of any legitimate protest that dares to
materialize out of the maze of theory. Local vigilantes have been
frequent and colorful additions to the progress of our enlightened
democracy which textbooks preach about. We have been tarring
and feathering nonconformists since the beginnings of the nation.
Lynching has also been an accepted form of liquidation, and not
only in the "racist" South. As late as 1933, Governor James
Rolph of California was still defending this unofficial form of mob
murder. When told about the lynchings of two suspected kidnap-

pers and murderers, he declared, "I believe it was a fine lesson for the whole nation. If anyone is arrested for the good job," he promised, "I'll pardon them all." A more subtle and sinister form of this great American custom was used in more recent years by law-enforcement officials in Chicago, Newark, and other cities to deal with uprisings in black ghettoes and other protest movements.

Americans are an inventive breed. Despite the fact that the violent and chaotic episodes in our history are usually overwhelmingly condemned, we've managed to develop a standard of hypocritical but elegant reaction to any conduct, however seedy, that is deemed politically or socially necessary. We outlaw general evil with all possible fanfare, but simultaneously declare that countless "white collar" crimes of less dramatic nature are not really identical and therefore treated in a gentle fashion.

Our attitude toward crime is likened to the devout man who liked to smoke. He asked his priest, "Father, can I smoke while I pray?" The good soul was shocked and emphatically forbade the practice. "Is it all right," the smoker then asked, "if I pray while I smoke?" That, the priest declared, was a downright pious thing to do. In much the same way, we the people, and therefore the government, can and do bend the law to suit our real or imagined needs, forsaking responsibility for our own lawlessness but dealing harshly with "crime" and calling constantly for "law and order." As recent disclosures in the Watergate case have adequately demonstrated, those who are loudest in their calls for "law and order" are ofttimes the most lawless.

The lack of responsibility on the government's part must inevitably lead, on the one hand, to repression and the abrogation of guaranteed civil rights and to vociferous protest, emotional demonstrations, and a growing gulf between the government and the governed, on the other. In such a tense and potentially explosive political and social atmosphere, judicial process is often "expedited" by political motives. Guilt is assumed if it is at all suspected. Much of the "revolutionary" history of the last decade is chockful of cases illustrating this contention. The problem which was never foreseen, however, is that lawlessness in government inevitably leads to an all-encompassing atmosphere of extralegal actions throughout the society. Strange things can occur in such an atmosphere, as recent cases of illegal narcotics raids illustrate.

In a raid on a private home in a big-city suburb, narcotics agents broke through the front door with guns drawn and immediately herded everybody inside off to jail. According to one of the agents, the unorthodox methods were adopted "because we believed the host to have hard narcotics—heroin, cocaine, you know." Was any of the hard stuff found? "No, but we found a couple of joints and booked them on that." One girl got off, another agent later confided, because she was pretty, it was her first offense, and she agreed to date him.

Not everyone is quite as lucky as this girl when narcotics agents knock or, in many cases, burst in without knocking. Fifteen burly policemen, toting assorted rifles and handguns, destroyed two doors and poured into William Pine's home on January 9, 1973. It was 10:00 A.M. and Mr. Pine, a thirty-eight-year-old night worker, was upstairs asleep. Mrs. Pine was caring for their thirteen-year-old daughter, Melody, home from school with a mild illness.

The men wore no badges, no uniforms, offered no identification, and were stonily silent, except for brusque commands to "sit down and shut up." Mrs. Pine and Melody, shoved onto the livingroom couch, were nearly hysterical seconds after the violent intrusion and could only scream over and over, "Please don't kill us, please don't kill us."

The screams had already roused Mr. Pine, who awoke to discover several guns trained on his bed and a gun barrel pressed against his head. "Don't move!" one of the men shouted. "Get up slowly and keep your hands over your head." He was violently pushed, still dressed only in his undershorts, out of the master bedroom and into the next room. Only after fifteen minutes of these stormtrooper tactics did the men bother to ask Mr. Pine his name. Then, as suddenly as they had entered, they departed, obviously confused. Mr. Pine rushed outside, following them, asking over and over who they were and what they wanted.

One of the men turned towards him briefly, muttered "state police," and left. Only later did the Pines discover that the police had actually wanted the house next door. A belated apology wasn't accepted very graciously. After all, tomorrow they had to go out to buy two new doors.

In an even more bizarre episode, roofing contractor John Conforti was finishing dinner when the doorbell rang in his $65,000 split-level home in Massapequa, Long Island. When he opened the door, two square-jawed agents of the Federal Bureau of Narcotics and Dangerous Drugs informed him they had a warrant to search his home for $4,000,000 in illegal profits from narcotics. Would he cooperate and tell them where the money was? Although he knew nothing about the money, or about narcotics for that matter, and told the agents that, it wasn't going to be his night. Twenty other agents, armed with sledgehammers, crowbars, and other wrecking tools, appeared out of the darkness. A nightmare was to begin for the Confortis, a nightmare that would never be forgotten.

It lasted twenty-four hours, a full day of wreckage that left the innocent family shocked and distraught. Paneling was pried from the walls, furniture broken in pieces, patio tiles uprooted, aluminum siding ripped off, gaping trenches dug in the yard. Even a toilet bowl was smashed to make sure the money was not hidden between the inner and outer casings. The whole unreal happening began to take on the appearance of a perverted, Felliniesque kind of circus, as dozens of neighbors gathered, children peeked in the windows, and the Good Humor ice-cream vendor set up shop on the front lawn.

John Conforti, forty-eight, has never been in trouble. No criminal record. Unfortunately for him and his family, his wife's brother, Louis Cirillo, had just been sentenced to twenty-five years in prison for narcotics peddling. After digging up $1 million in Cirillo's backyard, police got a tip from an informer that another

$4 million in booty was hidden somewhere in Conforti's house.

Despite this information, whether it was valid or invalid, Mr. Conforti's lawyer contended, "the search warrant says they can search—not search and destroy. This isn't Vietnam after all." Frank Monastero, the Bureau's associate regional director, didn't make anyone feel better when he voiced his reaction to the incident. Evidently his only gripe was that the agents failed to come up with the loot. "We didn't send a lot of guys in with instructions of 'you pound here' and 'you pound there,' " he maintained in an interview with *Time*. "We went through a series of progressive steps. Whether or not this was reasonable is up to the courts to decide. I personally felt that it was."

We do not contend that all narcotics agents are witless, sadistic heathens. The vast majority of law-enforcement officials on all levels of society are dedicated servants of the people, simply trying to clean up some of the dirtier parts of our society. What we find so incomprehensible in these various episodes, and the similar incidents which could be added to the long list, is that they seem to promote few horrified outcries, little reaction from the public or demands for stiffer protective legislation.

In many ways, the American public has been duped, lulled into a state of blissful unawareness, allowing the trampling of its civil rights to go on unchecked, unpunished, and unprotested.

Much of this process, literally a denial of political reality on the part of the American public, has been haphazardly generated by a succession of government administrations, law-enforcement agencies, and intelligence operatives. The atmosphere which allows demonstrators to be beaten can easily be brought to bear on anyone who threatens the rule of a certain administration. Watergate, again, is a prime example of this turn of events. Few incidents which fall into the gray area between the government's right to know and the people's right to privacy produced much ire before Watergate burst onto the scene. Yet the whole process, of which Watergate is just a minor part, continues unabated. Accepting governmental lawlessness as a matter of course is certainly conducive not to a free society, but to one which gradually relinquishes its freedoms and dies not with a bang, but a whimper.

The episodes of "oops, wrong house" raids and other terrifying occurrences are effects of the surveillance that has been conducted for years by government agencies and law-enforcement organizations. The tip of the iceberg has been seen, dissected, and duly reported to the people. The rest of the iceberg still exists and is growing under water. Allowing it to continue to grow leads to the syllogism, "Two wrongs don't make a right, but it makes for a lot of doubletalk." William Rehnquist, now a Supreme Court Justice, summarizing the doctrine before he was confirmed, told Senator Sam Ervin that although it would be "inappropriate" and "a waste of the taxpayer's money," it would not violate the senator's rights if the government put him under surveillance.

Apparently the Nixon Administration—of which Rehnquist was a part—agreed with this doctrine. But the Nixon Administration was not the first to be so inclined to place a number of surveillances on private citizens. Most of the surveillances have been based on sheerly political considerations, and, in the case of the Nixon Administration, the plan had been to restore "law and order" to America.

On a federal level, this surveillance can be roughly broken down into three categories or subgroups: (a) bureaucratic, (b) law-enforcement, and (c) military. A representative agency for each of these functions has been chosen in an attempt to understand just how and why the government feels it necessary to spy on its own citizens. Bureaucratic (in this section) is represented by the Internal Revenue Service, law-enforcement by the Federal Bureau of Investigation, and military by the army. An investigation of these individual agencies and their motives should clarify the general area of surveillance by the government in all its manifestations and disguises.

The Internal Revenue Service seems to be one of the more

inherently frightening members of the government bureaucracy. After all, anyone who is old enough to pay taxes is old enough to have his privacy invaded by overzealous agents engaged in "routine investigations" after the IRS computers begin to audit.

Audit! For many, just mentioning the dreaded word means inducing advanced shock.

Tax-evasion in the United States, alone among nations, is not an honorable sport. Here we pay taxes "voluntarily." Our government trusts us. We will yield up the just tithe of our labors for highways, courts, bombers, sewers, and the million and one other little costs our tax dollars go for. We are quick to declare that, of course, we pay these taxes out of a deep and abiding sense of civic responsibility and patriotism. After all, did not our Revolution start because of unfair taxation? And if the taxes we now pay are unfair, wouldn't we refuse to pay them?

Well, maybe some of us cheat a little? After all, if the President can get away with paying only a "nominal" amount of taxes, why can't we? (Well, he almost did.) But there still exists that very basic fear—that somewhere out there someone is listening and waiting for that ever-so-slight "mistake" of an undeserved deduction. In 1973, the shadowy IRS pounced on 1.7 million taxpayers, forcing them to fork over another $1.1 billion in taxes.

Returns are generally checked by a computer which has been programmed to compare certain line figures against certain others. The IRS audited a sample of ninety thousand returns and was therefore able to draw up limits against which percentage figures could be checked. If the ratio of charitable deductions to gross income, for example, exceeds these percentage limits, the auditor would assume that one of the two figures was incorrect. The computers are also programmed to automatically audit a certain percentage of returns from each income group. The actual percentages of each class that are audited are among the IRS's most closely guarded secrets.

The very idea of having one's returns audited may be bad

enough, but so long as a computer is the culprit, it almost seems bearable. But the computers do, unfortunately for some people, have some human help, and it is because an agent can "flag" a return for audit that people really begin to worry. An agent —human, full of foibles, problems, prejudices, and dislikes just like the rest of us—has an almost unlimited power to flag anyone's return for audit—and that can be frightening. It places a premium on not irritating agents indiscriminately. "Auditors, like anyone else, are human," one of the tax specialists noted. "My psychology tells me that a wise person should do everything in his power to be cooperative and not to antagonize the agent. I think it pays handsome dividends in the long run."

If your own reputation is not shady enough to arouse suspicion, your accountant's might be, and if he is known to certain agents as a little less than honest, you can more or less count on any return with his signature on it being flagged.

The IRS, like the police departments, has its own informant system, paying stoolies up to 10 percent of the extra money collected (on back, or other uncollected taxes) on the basis of their information. Although a lot of cranks might call, from disgruntled wives to jealous business rivals, the IRS Intelligence Division tries to weed out the phony from the serious. The rule, despite such screening, still seems to be: . . . when in doubt, audit.

The audit procedure is a complex process worked out after years of trial and error. Once a return has been selected for audit, it is handed over to one of the fifty-eight district offices which make up the IRS's seven regions. Group supervisors in the field offices assign the returns to the dozen or so examiners on their staff. The most complex cases go to *agents*, college graduates with degrees in accounting. The others go to *auditors*, college graduates but not accounting majors. If the examiner decides it is not necessary to audit a specific return, he asks his supervisor for permission to send it back to one of the ten Internal Revenue Service centers. The returns left for audit are handled in the order in which they were assigned. The examiner makes an appointment with the taxpayer and/or his tax-preparer. If your tax-preparer has been certified by the IRS or is a CPA or lawyer, he can represent you at any audit without your having to be present.

Once the actual meeting with the examiner begins, no taxpayer is totally prepared. The examiner has prepared his case previously. He knows what items he wants verified, what records he's going to require, what items he will disallow, what he thinks are "unusual" deductions and what he's going to challenge on legal grounds. You have no idea of what he's going to hit you with after he walks in. He might disallow a certain deduction. You disagree, and the fight begins. It all usually ends in some kind of compromise—you give in a little on some deductions, and he allows another.

If you disagree with the final assessment, you can appeal, depending on how much tax money is involved, how well you can document your case, and whether you have the time and the money to go through extended court proceedings. First step is a district conference, which can reverse, sustain, or partially sustain the original decision. If you are still dissatisfied after its judgment, you can appeal to the IRS Appellate Division and then appeal again in a civil court hearing. Naturally, you'd have to expend a lot of time, energy, and money to go through all of these proceedings. You might win the case and still lose money. Accountants and lawyers will charge you anywhere from twenty five dollars to one hundred dollars an hour for their time at these hearings. You have to take off time from work and take the time to prepare your case. It's not, to say the least, a pleasant experience.

Most people look at audits as a necessary evil and dismiss most of the horror stories that people tell about them (the IRS refuses to comment on any individual case) as fabrications or exaggerations. Some of the allegations from taxpayers are a little more serious and are not to be dismissed so lightly. In fact, Senator Joseph Montoya—Democrat of New Mexico, of Watergate fame—is also concerned with investigating reports from taxpayers who claim they have been bullied, hounded, and browbeaten by examiners whose methods sound more reminiscent of a loan shark collecting a bad debt the hard way.

Montoya alleged that there were charges that agents are trained to presume the taxpayer has cheated; that claiming the taxpayer owes too much rather than too little is a virtue rewarded by higher-ups; that two thirds of the money collected from audits each year was never owed at all; that wealthy taxpayers are far less likely to be audited than taxpayers who fall in the majority class ($10,000 or less income); and that politicians and prominent personalities have special pull with the IRS.

One couple who has gone through the auditing mill charged that the IRS sets a quota for squeezing money out of each of the taxpayers unfortunate enough to be targeted for an audit. Figures for 1972, according to these allegations, called for auditors to collect around $70 from individuals in the $10,000-and-under bracket, $926 from those in the $10,000-$30,000 range and $1,000 from businesses in the $100,000-$250,000 range.

The IRS refuses to reply to any of these charges. In fact, the IRS is one of the quietest agencies in the government. Rarely can taxpayers get copies of reports or information to which they are supposedly entitled. Rarely will the IRS answer their questions.

Philip Long, a real estate agent in Seattle, found this out to his chagrin after his own run-in with the IRS. After an audit of his 1966, 1967, and 1968 income tax returns, the agent claimed that he owed $38,144 in addition to $21,412 he had already had to pay. Long disagreed and decided to fight the judgment. He was curious about how the IRS had reached its conclusions and asked to study the agency's manuals on guidelines and other procedures.

Such data are supposed to be available to every American citizen under the Freedom of Information Act of 1966. Philip Long discovered that what he was entitled to in theory was awfully slow to materialize in practice. He filed 300 pages of legal briefs and spent over $10,000, even though he acted as his own attorncy, in an effort to secure relevant documents. Documents were produced one by one, accompanied by a lot of official grumbling, until two were left in dispute. Finally Seattle Federal Judge William Beeks decided that Long was entitled to these two documents as well. It was the first time the Freedom of Information Act had been used to successfully "prosecute" the IRS. The Service is still contesting the decision and the fight is not over. As Long remarked after the mentally harrowing and drawn out experience. "We've taken a few bricks out of the wall. We'd like to see a demolition job on the wall. But we have made progress."

Internal Revenue may be reluctant to publicize its inner workings, but it has never been known to be shy about wielding its powers against unwary taxpayers. During the Vietnam War era, many people stopped paying the federal tax on their phone bill as a method of protesting American involvement in Indochina. IRS didn't do much about the protest until the number of resisters mushroomed to more than 50,000 in 1971. Then they struck back. The IRS would take a lien for the few dollars it was owed and order the protester's bank to turn over the money—for which service the bank might charge as much as $20.00. Naturally the taxpayer paid the bank's service charge, not the IRS. If a bank account couldn't be located, the IRS looked for other assets. Bob Marcus from Boulder, Colorado, owed the kingly sum of $1.25. The IRS seized his Volkswagen, auctioned it for $277.00, deducted the government's share, and gave him the balance. It certainly seems like a lot of work for $1.25.

Yet if the sum involved is really important, the agency has a large arsenal of weapons it can throw into the fray. Under the guise of ferreting out tax-dodgers and racketeers, secret agents of the IRS can pry into the most intimate affairs, not only of those guilty of tax evasion and fraud, but of "suspected" innocents as well.

Although estimates of unreported income suggest that Americans voluntarily report 95 percent of their income, the IRS has the powers of a virtual dictator in its search for that other 5 percent. Agents have the authority to make prolonged investigations without ever bringing the case into a court for adjudication. Since there is no statute of limitations in a civil case, an individual could be harassed for years by an agent seeking some form of revenge—but yet never be formally charged with anything.

Revenue agents also have a virtual Open Sesame to anyone's most private financial records and papers in any of the nation's banks. By law, tax investigators are supposed to serve a summons upon the bank, specifically naming each record and document they wish to examine. In practice, however, most bankers allow the agents a surprising and unjustified latitude in going through just about any record or file in the bank's possession. If the agent does, for some strange reason, actually decide to take the unusual step of following the law, he files Levy Form No. 668-A. The taxpayer does not have to be informed of this fact by law and rarely is.

Section 7608 of the Internal Revenue Service Code gives agents even more sweeping powers. It empowers agents to completely dispense with arrest warrants if they feel an offense against the IRS has been committed in their presence or have reasonable grounds to believe a felony under such laws has been or is being committed. The term "reasonable grounds" is sufficiently vague to insure agents unlimited power to dispense "IRS justice" almost at will. Agents, based on this section, could conceivably arrest any taxpayer on suspicion at any time.

Section 7608 also allows the IRS to seize property, as in the case of Bob Marcus's Volkswagen, in order to settle outstanding tax indebtedness. Property, as it is defined in this statute, can include just about anything except your home and the gold fillings in your teeth. Agents are also empowered to enter any building during the day (or at night if it is unlocked) to examine any articles they believe might be suspect to federal taxation. Refusal to let them enter brings an instant $500 fine. Evidently a man's home is his castle only as long as there aren't IRS agents in the neighborhood.

These are still minor examples of the IRS habit of invading privacy to pay off Uncle Sam's debts. Internal Revenue is also a prime user of more covert methods of investigation and surveillance. According to a number of sources, IRS agents were using wiretaps as far back as 1942. Burke Young, a former agent, testified in a Senate subcommittee hearing that he was instructed in the various "arts" of overhearing conversations through bugging and wiretapping in 1942 by William Mellon. The former telephone worker, then an instructor for the IRS, was solely responsible for wiretapping and planting microphones at agents' request.

All of this activity was patently illegal. The Treasury Depart ment, of which the IRS is nominally a part, has banned wiretap- ping ever since 1938. Someone at Internal Revenue evidently decided the rule didn't apply to them. As Senator Edward V. Long remarked in a Senate hearing on IRS infractions, "Which of us would not believe that the regulation was made purely for show, to be winked at but not obeyed, when it was the national office of the Internal Revenue Service in Washington, D.C., that possessed and issued the wiretapping equipment, ran a wiretap school and also sent out the experts to install and remove the equipment?

"When they [agents] graduated from the school, they [the IRS] furnished them with a set of burglary tools, perhaps as a graduation present."

Reacting to these 1965 hearings, which sent ripples of rebellion through the ranks of ordinary taxpayers, President Johnson banned all wiretaps and electronic eavesdropping by federal employees, except in cases involving the national security. Yet on January 21, 1966, Alvin M. Kelley, the former district director of Boston, recently promoted to the Chicago office, told a Chicago *Daily News* reporter that the IRS would continue its eavesdropping *despite* the presidential order: "I would not like to give comfort," he haughtily declared, "to those who think we will not continue our use of intensive surveillance techniques."

Indeed, the Internal Revenue agents got even more intensive. According to newspaper accounts, the Internal Revenue Service in Cook County (Kelley's territory) began operating houses of pros- titution in 1970. Attorneys for an indicted police consultant charged in court that the conversations of persons who frequented the bawdy houses were electronically recorded by IRS agents. The agency denied all of the charges but would not comment on any of the details. Everything was hushed up, and no further details were ever published.

The 1965 Senate hearings, however, still had a few surprising findings to make public about covert Internal Revenue operations. Agents admitted under oath that it was common practice to intercept mail of defaulting taxpayers for possible evidence of hidden assets. Surprisingly, Representative Durward G. Hall testified that the IRS hadn't done the job alone. He reported that postal officials had admitted to him that they diverted personal, first-class mail to the IRS whenever it requested them to. The postal officials said all of the mail diverted belonged to tax-evaders and therefore no real harm was done.

The Senate didn't quite agree. As the result of the subcommittee hearings, a rider was attached to an act to reduce excise taxes then before Congress. Included as Section 82, the rider amended the IRS Code, prohibiting the seizure of first-class mail in transit for any reason whatsoever. Public Law 89-44 was passed by the 89th Congress and went into effect on June 21, 1965.

The IRS, ever inventive, was not to be completely foiled. It took up the practice of putting a "mail cover" on a suspect's correspondence. This merely consists of copying names, addresses, postmark, and date from all correspondence a "suspect tax-evader" receives. While not overtly damaging, you might lose a lot of the friends who write you, if they suddenly find themselves investigated by the IRS. If agents still have enough nerve to break the laws, they can always use a cytoscope, a small device that enables them to read the contents of a letter without opening it. Officials would not respond to questions on whether its agents regularly employed this device.

Even your friendly local library isn't immune to the IRS's investigations. Agents recently visited libraries in Atlanta, Maryland, and San Francisco, requesting the names of all persons who checked out books on Che Guevara or constructing homemade bombs. Evidently believing in the old maxim that you are what you read, an IRS spokesman said that they were concerned with forty or fifty suspects and wanted to develop additional leads. After the libraries refused to release the information and a number of journalists spread anti-IRS headlines across their newspapers and magazines, an IRS spokesman blandly remarked that the agency "does not look to the libraries as a significant source of continuing information."

The radical peace movement of the last decade led to the creation of a whole new unofficial arm in the IRS, sort of a "get the freaks" movement of their own. Churches became a special target of the antipeace agency. There are signs now that outspoken churchmen who opposed Nixon or his policies were still being pressured by zealous agents until very recently. "Since the beginning of this administration," noted a church spokesman, "the IRS has demonstrated an unprecedented interest in the civil rights, antipoverty, and antiwar activities of certain religious organizations." The biggest threat is to cancel the tax-exempt status of offending groups. Since churches are, for the most part, completely dependant on their tax free gifts, this is a very real and frightening threat for most of them.

Nevertheless, the activities and the IRS pressure continued. Dean M. Kelley of the National Council of Churches called it a "vendetta." A seventeen-page report released by the Guild of St. Ives in 1971 concluded, "there are indications that within the last two years the Internal Revenue Service has been investigating and, it is feared, attempting to restrict certain 'political' activities of churches and associations of churches."

The IRS's case is on slippery ground, loosely based on the pretext that according to the IRS code, no "substantial part" of the program of any tax-exempt organization can be used for "carrying on propaganda or attempts to influence legislation" or support individuals in political elections. Treasury regulations interpreting Section 501 (c) (3) of the Code have concluded that the following "charitable" activities are permissible:

Rehabilitation of the poor and distressed or of the under-privileged.
Advancement of religion, advancement of education or science.
Erection or maintenance of public buildings, monuments, or works.
Lessening of the burdens of government; and
Promotion of social welfare by organizations designed to accomplish any of the above purposes or:

1 to lessen neighborhood tensions;
2 to eliminate prejudice and discrimination;
3 to defend human and civil rights secured by law;
4 to combat community deterioration and juvenile deliquency.

The fact that any organization, in carrying out its primary purposes, advocates social or civil changes or presents opinion on controversial issues with the intent of molding public opinion or creating public sentiment to an acceptance of its views does not [disqualify an organization of exemption].

It would seem that according to these regulations, the IRS is opposing some of the very activities that the Treasury Department has decided are "fitting and proper" for a charitable organization to engage in. Despite this glaring contradiction, the IRS campaign has managed to continue and even found a few victims along the way. The Christian Action Council of South Carolina lost its exempt status in 1970 and was forced to pay retroactive taxes on its executive's salary, since the agency had decided he wasn't engaged in religious activity.

Other organizations have not yet lost the war, but they are getting worn down by the skirmishes at the front lines. The National Council of Churches was subjected to a long "routine" audit, which coincidentally followed the organization's stated opposition to the ABM system, a Nixon Administration brainchild. Their position evidently bothered conservative congressmen, and the probe was on.

The Episcopal Church was warned that continued use of its contributions for a student political education program would "jeopardize" its tax-exempt privileges. The IRS also instituted complete investigations of a student peace group's use of space in the Trinity Episcopal Church of Melrose, Mississippi, and the "political" activities of the California Migrant Ministry and the Florida Migrant Ministry, both of which had strongly supported Cesar Chavez and the United Farm Workers. The International Religious Foundation for Community Organizations (IFCO) was subjected to an eighteen-month-long audit. So were all of the black, Chicano, and poverty groups to which it regularly contributed. Finally, the United Church of Christ and the National Council of Churches were warned not to testify before a Senate subcommittee about legislation they both opposed. To do so, an agent intimated, would cost them their tax exemption.

Another "law and order" force which tends to form its own political mold is the Federal Bureau of Investigation, and given its basic right-of-center ideology, exhibits these tendencies in its reaction to political dissidents, specifically in the work it calls "national security cases," most of which are purely political in nature. Wrapped up in its self-proclaimed mission of waging a holy war against the radical forces at work in the nation's bowels, the more zealous agents of the Bureau might be sorely tempted to displace the passivity of data-collection in favor of more affirmative action. According to the evidence at hand, there is no doubt that this is what has occurred from time to time.

It is still almost impossible to determine how much of the Bureau's power and resources are devoted to surveillance of political dissidents and those involved in matters of national security. It is also difficult to give a detailed picture of the FBI's domestic surveillance machinery. Some estimates have put the manpower allocation as high as two thousand agents. Of the eight hundred documents taken in the raid on the FBI's Media, Pennsylvania, field office, 40 percent were concerned with political surveillance.

It is also hard to discover what criteria the Bureau uses to determine just what organizations and individuals become surveillance targets. No standards have ever been published by our self-styled (to a large extent) guardians of the national security. A little light is shed on the extent and nature of political surveillance by some of the facts and documents that have somehow managed to break through the Bureau's self-imposed pall of secrecy.

Fragmentary news stories, fourth-hand accounts from a friend of a friend, comments and details taken out of context, and unverified reports and charges from ex-agents and critics have left most people muddled under the barrage of confusing reports and statistics. The Bureau is one of the few unexplored regions left in our maddeningly shrinking world. Thus even when such items as the Media documents are suddenly made public, they are of necessity partially distorted because the Bureau still exists in an analytical vacuum. Any of these disclosures cannot be easily placed in the proper perspective or significantly studied in relation to the whole. Even the terminology employed must be explained to be understandable.

In Bureau lingo, there is a significant difference between "intelligence gathering" and "surveillance." The latter always refers to physical or electronic observation. If someone, for example, becomes a target of *surveillance*, his friends and associates will most likely be *investigated* as a matter of course. The bureau will *gather intelligence* about these associates, but only the original target will actually be under surveillance.

Senator Edmund Muskie, who attended a 1970 Earth Day rally,

revealed an FBI report on the event in April 1971. Only Rennie Davis (a defendant in the Chicago Seven conspiracy trial) was literally under surveillance, according to the report on "National Environmental Actions, April 22, 1970," but in the process of that investigation, the Bureau "gathered intelligence" on most of the other people on the speakers' platform, including Senator Muskie himself.

"Mission" and "coverage" are terms referring to the aims and objectives of the Bureau in a specific intelligence effort. A mission is evidently administered into existence by the issuance of an LHM, or Letter Head Memorandum, written for dispersal to the proper individuals and departments within the Bureau and for certain limited release to other agencies of the government. When LHMs are prepared, they are generally accompanied by a more detailed administrative memorandum, *not* released outside the Bureau, which delineates the reasons for the proposed action, sources consulted, and specific procedural suggestions.

The LHMs could go into details such as the reports of various undercover agents associated with the subject group, summarized press releases and publications of the group, data linking them to subversive individuals or organizations, and any miscellaneous observations by agents.

A primary outside beneficiary of most of these reports is the Analysis and Evaluation Unit of the Justice Department's Internal Security Division, a group that closely follows every organization which might be even vaguely involved with any protest demonstrations or other actions. They also assist other officials in the Division with a periodic review of all organizations with a connection to any of the subversive or extremist groups on the Attorney General's list.

All of the names which appear in these reports do not automatically become new files in the FBI's national computer data bank, but since all of them are crossreferenced at the field office or headquarters level anyway, memoranda in which the names are mentioned can always be recovered despite the lack of a separate index number. The effect is the same even if the means are slightly different.

The "everyday" criminal investigation has a specific beginning, middle, and end. Unfortunately, the Bureau's investigations always have a specific beginning, but not always a noticeable end. Many of its agents are involved in an ongoing investigatory process, questioning and developing information about individuals and groups that the Bureau deems dangerous. There is little or no distinction in the Bureau's statutory authorization or in its own declarations between what it considers its responsibility in a normal, limited investigation and the on-going intelligence operation.

After a long history of perfecting its surveillance techniques, the FBI was able to throw the full panoply of investigative hardware and abilities into its battle against political dissidents. Agents questioned friends, relatives, employers, fellow employees, banks, school officials, neighbors, landlords, acquaintances, and anyone else who could shed light on the motives or activities of the person they were investigating.

Besides its ever-resourceful agents, the Bureau also has at its disposal, as previous chapters have described, an incredibly varied array of wiretaps, bugging gear, photographic equipment, and tailing devices to keep track of the people they are interested in knowing more about.

The really vigorous agents on the payroll might go so far as to inspect your garbage, copy return addresses from incoming mail, place informers or undercover agents in any club or organization, or search any premises. All of the data collected through all of these devices are placed, raw, unevaluated in a dossier. Periodic reports are made summarizing relevant material in the most significant of these dossiers.

While many of these techniques of collecting intelligence are common to most law-enforcement agencies and private detective firms throughout the world, the FBI, in this area of its jurisdiction, is not concerned with criminals at all; rather the vast power commanded by our national police force is being used to keep tabs on the legitimate political activities of American citizens who are innocent of any crime.

Some of those who inevitably find their way into the files of the supercomputerized FBI are suspected of some violation of federal statutes which fall into the Bureau's vast jurisdiction. These laws cover almost the whole spectrum of action into which political activities might fall: the Internal Security Act of 1950, which created a new system for listing "subversive" organizations and the new titles to go with it—Communist-action, Communist-front, and Communist-infiltrated—laws against espionage, sabotage, and sedition, especially the Smith Act; laws covering the deportation of aliens for a variety of purely political reasons; recently enacted legislation prohibiting interstate traffic with the intention of blowing up buildings, to promote or participate in a riot or similar activities; and the federal loyalty-security program, which requires that the employment of a federal job applicant be "clearly consistent with the interests of national security." The federal program authorizes the Attorney General to maintain a list of "totalitarian, Fascist, Communist or subversive" organizations. These provisions, taken together, enable the Federal Bureau of Investigation to launch inquiries into almost any area of political conduct its whim or fancy might dictate.

An organization needn't be blatantly subversive to fall into the Bureau's surveillance web. Entirely legal and above board groups with only a marginal interest in political activity might suddenly be inundated with a large influx of squeaky-clean, crewcut new members. The new and enthusiastic converts are, in reality, your friendly undercover agents.

Even totally innocent and nonsubversive groups are not free of overzealous infiltrators. After all, the agents reason, the group, though outwardly unthreatening, may be inadvertently harboring dangerous subversives or radical extremists in its midst. Anybody and any organization fits into the vague category such actions define and therefore qualifies as a legitimate target of inquiry. Even one subversive member could add them to the Attorney

General's ever-lengthening list of Communist-infiltrated organizations.

As J. Edgar Hoover once put it, "We, of course, do not investigate labor unions. . . . We have, however, investigated innumerable instances of Communist infiltration into labor unions." Even an FBI agent would find it difficult, we believe, to explain the distinction. Searching out "subversive activities" and the FBI's legendary obsession with loyalty and security insures a never-ending chain of suspicion, surveillance, and investigation.

The chain seems to be forged with solid steel links. The investigation of even an innocent individual can (and usually does) lead to an almost infinite number of spinoff investigations of friends, acquaintances, relatives, associates, organizations and clubs he frequents, and even the leaders and members of these groups. A single inquiry, in the blink of an eye, is suddenly a thousand. For example, checking out an alleged member of the Communist party inevitably led to "fellow travelers," "pseudoliberals," "dupes" and any associates of *these* new investigative targets.

If an investigation actually produced enough information to enable the government to press criminal charges, a rare occurrence at best, the defendant also had to deal with Hoover's special penchant for prejudging their cases. He did it with the Berrigan brothers. Earlier he launched a personal attack on Dr. Martin Luther King. Damaging material from the Bureau's files on San Francisco Mayor Joseph Alioto were given to *Look* magazine. Hoover even attempted at one point to get a Trans World Airlines pilot discharged, according to Senator George McGovern, because he had dared to criticize the Bureau's methods in a hijacking episode. The FBI casually informed the airline that the pilot had "experienced some personal difficulty in the Air Force prior to his employment by TWA."

Harassment can always take far more subtle forms, like photographing everyone in the vicinity of a political rally or peaceful demonstration. Many of us active in the civil rights movement in the last decade remember the straight-looking guys with the cameras who indiscriminately shot pictures of everybody in the area, demonstrators and innocent bystanders alike. The other agents who forsook camera for pen and notebook were also frequent visitors. The well-publicized political conspiracy trials which were often a result of agent infiltrators in the ranks were often put forward by Bureau apologists as proof of the necessity of such practicies.

Not all of the methods employed by the FBI were even remotely legal or defensible. There are, indeed, numerous instances of FBI conduct that were patently illegal and occasionally unconstitutional as well. Extensive bugging and wiretapping, always questionable practices at best, were nevertheless Standard Operating Procedure in the post-World War II era, as the historical survey in the first chapter detailed.

But agents have been known to intercept—and occasionally open—United States mail. The agents' term for it is "camphoring." Other cases involve agents who would, like common thieves, enter private homes and search and scize personal and household effects without a legal search warrant.

The very existence of a vast investigatory apparatus like the FBI would lead many to believe such actions a foregone conclusion. Yet even the many publicized accounts of illegal activity are only the tip of a gruesome iceberg, since most instances of abuse are rarely acknowledged by the otherwise astute corps of public relations personnel who polish the Bureau's image.

Certainly President Nixon never made the mistake of underestimating Hoover's power—or his willingness to use it if he thought a show of strength was in order. According to recently released transcripts of presidential conversations, Nixon considered Hoover a "crony" and "a tough (expletive deleted)."

"Hoover performed," Nixon gushed in one recorded conversation. "He would have fought. That was the point. He would have defied a few people. He would have scared them to death. He had a file on everybody."

Assignments which involve illegal breaking and entering, burglary, and other covert activities are known among agents as "black bag jobs." Though some details of these operations had come out in past press coverage, the real extent of the Bureau's use of such covert operations was not known until it was inadvertently revealed in relation to the Watergate hearings. The American public was suddenly informed that over a thirty year period ending in 1966, agents of the FBI periodically burglarized homes, apartments, offices, and embassies seeking foreign intelligence, clues in criminal cases, and evidence against suspected organized crime figures or political dissidents.

At a San Clemente news conference, President Nixon shocked reporters by referring to what he called "a quite well known" string of "authorized" burglaries undertaken by the Bureau over the years. Justice Department officials who served during the Kennedy and Johnson years substantiated his assertions, revealing that such practices had existed "since the days of FDR," in the words of one spokesman.

The burglaries were nicknamed "black bag jobs" because of the valises filled with burglars' tools the agents carried with them on the assignments. Everything from lockpicking gear to electronic eavesdropping equipment was supplied them by the Bureau. According to one ex-agent, when their instructor gave them the tools, he reminded them jokingly not to get caught since "possession of burglary tools is against the law in Washington, D.C."

Agents on such an assignment knew when they prepared that, as far as the Bureau was concerned, they were private citizens for the duration of the job. They knew that if they were caught, the ever-loyal Bureau, in the best tradition of spy organizations everywhere, would not only refuse them any aid but would fail to even acknowledge their existence. They were alone. Never could an agent claim that he was "just following orders" like a good soldier.

The rule on such missions, according to one official, was "Never take anything except information!" A missing piece of evidence or a purloined notebook were just a little too obvious. Of course, a bug could always be *left*. The rule didn't say anything about *leaving* anything, now did it?

According to the same official, bag jobs carried out in domestic cases were never authorized by anyone outside the FBI. This would explain the reactions of former Attorneys General Nicholas DeB. Katzenbach and Ramsey Clark when they were apprised of Mr. Nixon's comments on the "well known" string of burglaries. Both denied any knowledge of any such occurrences. One must assume that, like their predecessors, they were simply never told about the operations. It is not a very difficult assumption to swallow.

The full implications of the Bureau's indiscriminate investigation of whatever group it feels like looking into are revealed only when its internal workings are inadvertently exposed to public view. The twenty-year-old Coplon documents report the surveillance, for example, of actor Fredric March and his wife, a music student who visited his mother at the New Jersey headquarters of the Communist party, and a young man connected with a pro-Israeli group that sent representatives to various parts of the world, among other dangerous criminals.

After studying these documents, the National Lawyers Guild summary concluded:

> It is, then, perfectly plain that, by and large, the FBI investigations described in the Coplon reports were attempting to determine not what crimes the subject had committed, but what kind of a person he was with reference to his social, political and economic views, his personal associations, and his organizational affiliations. The Coplon investigations demonstrate that the FBI investigates persons in order to determine whether they have radical views and associations.

Hoover himself gave some indication of the extent of the Bureau's political surveillance in budget hearings before Congress. In 1960, he testified, "We now have 155 known, or suspected, Communist-front and Communist-infiltrated organizations under investigation." Only two years later, the figure had already swelled to "some 200."

It is important to note that these are not Communist-*action* groups—those organizations, at least according to the FBI, which are composed solely of fanatical anarchists and radicals dedicated to violently overthrowing the United States Government and ruining the American Way of Life. The groups Hoover was talking about might be as innocent as the Quakers, as "conservative" in outlook as the NAACP. Yet their innocence or guilt of *any* charges (none of which were ever filed) will never really be determined. Guilt is virtually assumed when the Bureau points its accusing finger, adding them to the list of "Cominfil" (suspected Communist infiltration) organizations.

The FBI, despite its ranks of public relations experts which place it only slightly below God's heavenly legions in moral fortitude and divine right, is still a political police force, covering over illegal acts with glowing press releases that cite endless statistics which are supposed to verify its claim to the title of "Number One Crimefighter."

The Bureau would still have us believe that their critics are maligning them unfairly, focusing on insignificant, minor, and unrepresentative events and blowing the molehills out of proportion. The myth even persists in some circles that the FBI is somehow *not* a political organization, since Hoover was always supposed to be "above politics." Unfortunately, at least for these wishful thinkers, the whole basic ideology of the Bureau places it squarely in the position of fighting a political war with political weaponry on a purely political level.

The Bureau still persists in its low estimation of the political sophistication of the American people, naively believing them too easily misled by radical political propaganda. Given this unrealistic view of the political scene, it is a small step for the Bureau to make in crowning itself the guardian of the nation's political well-being.

All of the documentation of the Bureau's behavior lends little credence to the FBI's belatedly and lamentably lame appeal for understanding.

The organization is not, and never has been, simply a machinelike gatherer of information which acts merely as a funnel for the data its agents compile. It determines what to collect and how to get it, evaluates the information, and passes on only the portions it considers relevant to other government agencies, private agencies, law-enforcement organizations, and anyone else with a "need to know." These operations are far from mechanical.

Throughout this whole process of investigation, no one in the FBI seems to realize that people's lives are intimately affected simply because the FBI is asking questions about them.

The very public relations machinery that is used so effectively to contradict critics is also a potent weapon in the Bureau's war against radical politicians and their supporters. Hoover personally defended Senator Joseph McCarthy against his many critics. When George McGovern ran against incumbent Karl Mundt in South Dakota's Senate race, Hoover calculatingly released a letter praising Mundt's anti-Communism. Senator Eugene McCarthy, not quite as much a Bureau favorite as his namesake, dared to announce his intention, should he be elected President, to replace Hoover as director. Hoover, never particularly well-known for accepting criticism graciously, responded to McCarthy in the *Federal Bureau of Investigation Bulletin*: "All Americans should view with serious concern the announced intentions and threats by a political candidate, if elected, to take over and revamp the FBI to suit his own personal whims and desires."

In many ways, the very existence of dossiers on various Congressmen acted to dissuade most politicians from the kind of "heresy" voiced by McCarthy. The existence of the dossiers became a potent political force for Hoover. So long as someone thinks the FBI has information that it *could* release about them if it wanted to, they are understandably intimidated. The information, of course, will probably never be disseminated. The threat of disclosure, a kind of official, bureaucratic blackmail, is enough for most.

Not surprisingly, the Bureau places few limitations on the types of information it allows its agents to collect on individuals and organizations and enter in their dossiers. It's difficult to find any information that these agents deem too irrelevant to pay attention to. Aided by the generous sprinkling of wiretaps, bugs, informers, and undercover reports, evidently every possible shred of information, no matter how small or inconsequential, goes into creating a new dossier.

The Coplon and Media documents point out just how irrelevant much of this information really is. A few of the activities which were considered serious enough to place an individual into the investigative files were outlined by the National Lawyers Guild committee report:

> Being affiliated with the (Henry Wallace) Progressive Party
> Admiring the military feats of the Russian Army during World War II
> Acting (in 1945) in a skit about the battles of Leningrad and Stalingrad
> Opposing the House Committee on Un-American Activities
> Writing a master's thesis on the New Deal in New Zealand
> Attending a rally against the Mundt bill

These are only the first six items on a substantially longer list.

The more contemporary Media, Pennsylvania, documents include details of the investigation of a Swarthmore College philosophy professor who invited "controversial speakers" to the campus, was visited by "hippie types," and had printing equipment in his garage, presumably to turn out tons of subversive literature to spread around the campus. Information was later turned up by independent investigators of the FBI that the professor was actually being vaguely linked with two alleged bank robbers and a murder perpetrated by a radical political group. Neighbors, the college's security officer and switchboard operator, the local postmaster and police chief were all questioned by agents investigating this "connection." All of them promised the agents they would keep the professor and his mail, telephone, and movements "under surveillance."

Such actions might not be illegal, but they certainly point out that the side effects of any FBI investigation cannot be airily dismissed.

The Media documents also listed the names of all identifiable individuals at meetings of a black church group and noted that a Villanova University priest had borrowed a monastery car (which they learned from a lay brother at Villanova Monastery) and that a student under investigation majored in Greek. Other sources confirm that these few examples of data the FBI deems necessary and relevant are not atypical of its routine operations. Once the Bureau is interested in you, the inquiry can roll in any direction. It is left purely to an agent's whim and fancy.

After four decades with Hoover, FBI agents have had to contend with three directors and five Attorney Generals. L. Patrick Gray 3rd, who succeeded Hoover, was quick to promise to "open the window" to the press and public. He did, in fact, first let women join the bureau, unthaw the relationship with a hostile press inured to Hoover's noncooperation, and encourage long hair, colored shirts, and black agents . . . none of which his predecessor would have tolerated in his wildest moments.

But Gray, for all his niceties, evidently didn't have the confidence of the people in power. In the White House-released transcript of a conversation with John Dean III, President Nixon candidly conceded that Gray was "just quite stubborn and . . . not very smart." Nixon's lifelong love affair with "the Bulldog" had built up an image in Nixon's mind which clashed all too obviously with that which Gray presented—judging from these deprecating remarks.

Nixon probably would have added an ''(expletive deleted)'' on two to the tapes if he had discovered early on his acting director's clandestine involvement with the Washington *Post*, not a huge favorite with the administration by any means. Gray, according to highly placed newspaper sources, was the mysterious ''source'' who helped Bob Woodward and Carl Bernstein with their initial blockbuster reportage of the Watergate affair. If true, it shows Gray to be not as stupid as Nixon thought, nor as malleable.

After the short term of Gray's reign and, William Ruckelshaus's stopover, Kansas City Police Chief Clarence M. Kelley, an FBI veteran, was confirmed as the second director in FBI history. Ruckelshaus and former Attorney General Elliot Richardson had already begun a series of delicate maneuvers designed to radically reform the Bureau. They succeeded in getting Kelley to continue the maneuvers. Kelley also agreed to work with the Attorney General more closely than Hoover had previously done.

A Ruckelshaus memo to Kelley outlined eleven issues which were considered ''by no means exhaustive but a good starting point,'' in defining the FBI's major investigative thrust: (a) Wiretaps and surveillance; (b) should law-enforcement and intelligence-gathering within the Bureau be separated? (c) what is the statutory basis of the Bureau's intelligence network? (d) term of FBI Directors; (e) relationship of FBI to the Justice Department; (f) if the FBI is to remain part of the Department, what is the relationship between the director and the Attorney General? (g) legal and illegal investigation techniques—role of congressional oversight; (h) files and disclosure—what's the system? (i) should a civilian review board be established to ''watchdog'' the Bureau's intelligence-gathering? (j) relations with other government agencies; (k) should foreign officers report directly to the FBI director?

Richardson's resignation and Ruckelshaus's abrupt dismissal in the wake of the Cox firing, the so-called Saturday Night Massacre, seem to have abruptly ended the campaign for reform. Richardson's successor as Attorney General, William Saxbe, had an early penchant for commenting on the FBI's progress in various cases (the Hearst kidnapping is a notable example) but apparently little interest in radically altering the way the Bureau functions. Kelley is on his own, it appears.

Kelley, unchecked and unmonitored, could be good or bad. No one is giving out odds yet. In appearance, at least, he presents a sharp contrast to his predecessor, whom even his kindest critics characterized as having an abrasive and uncompromising personality. Kelley, on the other hand, comes on with a kind, fatherly image, guileless and unassuming. He seems sincere when he admits to college audiences that "no organization is perfect—we are geared to change." Even his choice of platforms has added to his image. After a recent speech at Harvard, one police officer gushed, "Hoover always spoke before very friendly audiences. But not Kelley. He wants to talk to the Bureau's natural enemies."

So far, after a year as director, Kelley's reforms seem more tinsel than concrete. Outwardly, the Bureau has changed little. The Hoover hierarchy has been whittled down a bit and Kelley's years as a police chief have apparently taught him the value of cooperation with other law-enforcement agencies. The press hasn't exactly been given the run of the place, but Kelley has evidently tried to keep the window that Gray had opened—open. He has also established a Division of External Affairs to deal with the media.

Sympathetic Kelley-watchers contend that the real changes will be internal (and therefore hard to evaluate), essentially a product of Kelley's "different way of doing things." They predict that his self-projection as a nonideological law-enforcement administrator ("He's not out to get anybody") will readily translate into tangible reforms.

It's too soon to tell just where Kelley is headed and how he plans to get there. In a 1974 speech at Harvard he revealed a surprisingly familiar ideological naiveté. Kelley contended that the most dangerous threat to American internal security was the violence of the "so-called New Left," which is virtually nonexistent. Kelley even raised the specter of the Red Menace that served Hoover so well, arguing that the threat of foreign spies was greater now than ever.

"Compared to Hoover, he looks great," a Harvard professor commented. "But I felt he missed the issues. He did not grasp the essence of what people were saying. It is a curious kind of response you get from police—an assumption that if agents do something wrong it is not because they were told to do so. There is an implicit trust in structure and procedure. The real issue is what happens despite procedure."

What has happened in the past is well-documented fact. Whether Kelley will continue the practices of Hoover while outwardly calling for "change" and "reform" will only become evident in the years to come.

From the pseudomilitary of the FBI we go now to the real military, and to another tremendous force of law and (military) order. At one point, it appeared tthat the military was competing with the FBI in striving to keep the greatest number of civilians under a watchful eye.

In mid-September 1969 rumors of a large demonstration brewing outside the gates of Fort Carson, Colorado, drew a number of agents from the military intelligence units. The demonstration was far less dangerous than anticipated. In fact, of the 119 demonstrators who participated in the paceful protest, 53 were undercover agents. Six helicopters were hovering over the whole scene, but they made so much noise that the agents on the ground couldn't tape the speeches the antiwar agitators were making. It sounds like something right out of the Keystone Kops, but the case wasn't unique, unfortunately.

If not for certain legislators who believed that the rights of the people came before the fears of the military, the gruesome and complex story of such military surveillance of American citizens might never have been made public.

The Senate Subcommittee on Constitutional Rights has been in the forefront of the battle since the early 1960s, when it first began to study the right of privacy as part of its mandate to "examine, investigate and make a complete study of any and all matters pertaining to constitutional rights."

Although it wound up investigating a number of separate factual issues, the thrust of the subcommittee inquiry was to identify and end unwarranted intrusions by the government into the privacy of individual citizens. Inquiries were conducted into the rights of federal employees (1967), the use of certain questionnaires by the Bureau of Census (1968), the Secret Service (1969), and an HEW questionnaire (1969).

It was against this background that the subcommittee conducted its investigation of Army surveillance. The detailed study was set off by an article entitled "CONUS Intelligence: The Army Watches Civilian Politics," published in the January 1970 *Washington Monthly*. Written by Christopher H. Pyle, a former captain in Army Intelligence, the article alleged that the Army had made it standard operating procedure to maintain files on the activities and inner workings of almost every radical and extremist group in the country.

This data collection, Mr. Pyle charged, had its origins in the Army's preparation for riot duty, but had gone well beyond the need for reconnaissence of cities to the development of personality and organizational files on individuals and groups totally unassociated with violent political protests. What was particularly unique about the data banks was that they were devoted to storing information about the lawful activities of civilians completely unaffiliated with the Armed Forces.

The publication of the article and the resulting howls that were heard even in the halls of the Capitol prompted the subcommittee to raise some serious questions in its hearings. Was the Army really spying on civilians? If so, was it properly authorized by law to engage in such surveillance? To what extent did this domestic surveillance infringe upon the constitutional rights of politically active individuals and organizations? What has been—or could be—the impact of military spying on the freedoms of speech, press, religion, and association, the rights to privacy and due process of law, and the right to petition one's government for redress of grievances?

Correspondence suddenly became hot and heavy between the subcommittee members, the Department of the Army, and the Department of Justice. The process was slow. Initial denials slowly became partial admissions. Requests for directives or for examples of intelligence operations were belatedly and reluctantly honored. Subcommittee hearings began in February and March 1971 and were published under the title "Federal Data Banks. Computers and the Bill of Rights" in January 1972. It took fifteen months, however, before the efforts of the subcommittee chairman, Senator Sam Ervin, forced the Pentagon to free the staff report on military surveillance, which was finally released and published in August 1973.

Military surveillance of civilian politics in the United States is as old as Army intelligence itself. Although the precedents go back to colonial times, the Army's most recent operations can be directly traced from the founding of military intelligence in 1917. From the outset, the new group of amateur sleuths competed with the Department of Justice for jurisdiction to investigate spies, saboteurs, and other subversives within the civilian populace.

By the end of World War II, Army intelligence had successfully set up its own system of nationwide informants. These civilians not only reported to the Army suspected German spies and sympathizers, but also gave detailed information about labor organizers, socialists, Communists, aliens, and even U.S. attorneys who supposedly lacked sufficient anti-German fervor.

Although fear of labor strife, socialism, and communism prevented the immediate dissolution of the Army's domestic intelligence network, it was finally abandoned in 1924 as other agencies within the government (mainly the FBI) took over.

The establishment of the Army Counter Intelligence Corps (CIC), just prior to World War II, marked the creation of the intelligence-gathering organization which is really the object of the current controversy. By the end of the war, each of the stateside offices of the CIC was issuing spot reports, weekly and monthly intelligence summaries, and a variety of special reports on civilian political activities.

Most observers of the recent growth of the intelligence network agree that the expansion grew mainly out of the use of troops to enforce federal laws and court orders in the South and to put a stop to ghetto riots in the early 1960s. Intelligence records have been discovered that date back to 1962 in some cities.

In response to such events as the Newark and Detroit riots in 1967, the march on the Pentagon, and the April 1968 riots following the assassination of Dr. Martin Luther King, the Army made the decision to engage in full scale monitoring of domestic political activities. Although there is considerable evidence that a number of high-level conferences were held to determine how the federal government should respond to riots and demonstrations, the Defense Department's refusal to cooperate with any effort to get at the roots of this expansion make it nearly impossible to discover what really happened. The Senate subcommittee was forced to admit that it is still uncertain who directed military intelligence to collect such vast amounts of personality and organizational files.

For the most part, the Army relied on existing intelligence structures to carry out its CONUS (for Continental United States) intelligence mission. The principal collection agencies were the U.S. Army Intelligence Command (USAINTC) and the Continental Army Command (CONARC). The Counterintelligence Analysis Branch (CIAB) was the chief analysis unit. The Directorate for Civil Disturbance Planning and Operations (DCDPO) also produced its own analysis and computerized listings of future demonstrations. A discussion of the organization of each of these groups follows:

U.S. Army Intelligence Command

From its creation in January, 1965, USAINTC was the Army's chief domestic intelligence collection agency. Its three hundred-odd offices spanned the continent and provided over one thousand trained counterintelligence agents for the task.

The forty-eight continental United States (Alaska and Hawaii were regarded as overseas commands) were divided into six multistate areas. Each was serviced by a Military Intelligence Group. Each MI Group, with one exception, was organized into regions, field offices, and resident offices. The exception was the 116th MI Group, which covered the military district of Washington from its offices outside the gates of Fort Lesley J. McNair.

The group and region headquarters, for the most part, were command posts and administrative centers. They levied investigative requirements, reviewed agents' reports, and collated the results before sending them to the Fort Holabird data bank. Most of the actual investigative manpower was located in the field and resident offices, which differed only in size and in the sensitivity of the records it might store. Most of the CONUS intelligence files were held at the region or group level.

U.S. Continental Army Command

The Continental Army Command was the giant "holding company" which provided general supervision and coordination for most of the Army's stateside units; its principal components were the five U.S. armies stationed in the United States. Headquarters for this agency was Fort Monroe, near Hampton, Virginia.

CONARC's chief preoccupation was supervising and training troops. They also maintained troop reserves in readiness for immediate deployment in crises overseas or at home. To prepare these troops for riot duty, CONARC's commanding general turned to his intelligence personnel, the G-2 offices, and directed them to step up their collection of domestic intelligence.

The chief collectors of CONUS intelligence within the Continental Army Command appear to have been counterintelligence agents assigned to MI detachments. These agents are the "action army" counterparts of the Army Intelligence Command's special agents. Though their main job is to handle internal personnel, document, and security problems of the division to which they are attached, these duties aren't all that time-consuming. The sections were therefore easily able to absorb the additional task of monitoring civilian political activity off post. In this role, they sometimes entered into direct competition with agents from the local office of the Intelligence Command.

Although the normal strength of a counterintelligence section is only nine men, the CI section at Fort Carson, Colorado, "grew to over thirty men," according to former intelligence agent Laurence F. Lane. "The tactical responsibilities of the on-post counterintelligence operation were minimal," he stated, "while the section was extremely overstrength. The answer was to use these men to monitor the activists in the community."

Counterintelligence Analysis Branch

Since the fall of 1967, if not earlier, the CIAB has functioned as the chief producer of CONUS intelligence analyses and predictions for the Pentagon. Through its briefings of high military and civilian officials, and its contributions to the Undersecretary of the Army's "Black Book" of intelligence items, CIAB has exercised a major influence on the course of civil disturbance decision-making.

As the chief analysis unit for the Army's assistant chief of staff for intelligence, CIAB's mandate is worldwide. The preparation of reports on domestic civil disorders apparently began around 1964, when the North American desk was created. Through subsequent reorganizations, this desk eventually evolved into a full-fledged domestic intelligence section with "leftwing," "rightwing," and "racial" desks. The section was also known as the "counterespionage/countersubversion" desk by some agents.

By the fall of 1968, the number of CIAB personnel assigned to monitor domestic disturbances and dissent exceeded that assigned to monitor counterintelligence matters emanating from any other part of the world, including Indochina.

Directorate for Civil Disturbance Planning and Operations

Following the April 1968 riots, plans were announced to create a special 180-man command center in the Pentagon capable of directing twenty-five ten-thousand-man civil disturbance task forces simultaneously. DCDPO was born. It was lodged in a "domestic war room" in the cavernous basement storeroom beneath the Pentagon's mall parking lot. The $2.7 million for its construction was paid for out of the Joint Chiefs' Contingency Fund, thus obviating the necessity for congressional approval.

The equipment in the new war room on civilians included extensive teletype networks to MI group emergency operation centers throughout the country, situation maps, closed-circuit television, hot lines, an illuminated switchboard, and a computerized data-processing center. Like the Intelligence Command, its "watch teams" operated around the clock.

At this point, a word should be said about the Justice Department's system for collecting civil-disturbance intelligence, which in many ways the Army duplicated. Until early 1970, Army reports made a substantial contribution to the Justice Department's intelligence system. Other sources of information include the ninety-four U.S. Attorneys, the Border Patrol, the Secret Service, and the Passport Office. The bulk of the information received by these analysts, however, has always come from the FBI and the press.

The chief analytical unit in this system was the Interdivisional Intelligence Unit. Like the CIAB, its Army counterpart, the IDIU was called upon to produce summaries of past civil disorders, listings of expected demonstrations, predictions concerning the likelihood of violence, and reports on individuals and organizations thought to be involved.

The collection of information was not restricted to events involving immediate dangerous activity or those having a potential for violence. Instead, surveillance and data-collection covered a wide spectrum of activity and information, including the most minor and innocuous behavior, as part of the process of obtaining complete dossiers on the individuals and organizations targeted.

Under Attorney General Ramsey Clark, the IDIU was a low-budget operation employing only three or four persons. When John Mitchell stepped in, however, its functions were increased and its role broadened. By Spring 1970, according to a report by Morton Kondracks of the Chicago *Sun-Times*, it had acquired a $274,000 budget, twelve intelligence analysts, and a domestic war room.

Witnesses before the Senate subcommittee would not comment on this development, but James T. Devine, chief of the IDIU until early 1971, is quoted as saying that the information available through the IDIU computer was chiefly utilized to decide whether or not to prosecute certain participants in demonstrations. He conceded that "the data was of practically no value as a barometer in assessing the chance of civil disorder in any given city, one of the purposes for which the unit was formed in 1967."

The Army was also an integral part of the Justice Department's civil disturbance intelligence structure. Membership on both of the standing committees within the Department that supervised the entire intelligence operation always included a representative of the Army. This participation reflected not only the admission that the Army would be the agency called upon to suppress any civil disturbance, but also the judgment that Army intelligence should remain a part of the intelligence effort.

Military intelligence officers, as a matter of fact, strongly resisted the efforts of their civilian superiors to transfer all responsibility for collecting intelligence to the Justice Department. They argued that the Justice Department system was both unable and unwilling to collect the type of intelligence the Army needed to carry out its functions. They instead stressed the superior resources of Army intelligence and the urgency of the situation.

The Army's position might be simply viewed as a product of its desire to preserve a system and program which by this time was quite extensive. In any event, the excuse for the original military involvement—the superior Army resources and the urgency of the situation—became the rationale for continuing military intelligence operations despite the establishment of the Justice Department machinery.

In 1967 and 1968, the Army's arguments appear to have carried great weight at the Justice Department. Thus, however inappropriate the use of Army agents to watch political protests might have seemed, there was little resistance from the Justice Department to their continued participation. In drafting a civil disturbance action plan for the President, the Justice Department tried to get the Army to provide a statement outlining its responsibility for intelligence-collection under the plan.

Met with the Army's refusal to "tie itself down," and its own reluctance to take sole responsibility, the Department settled for a general statement that intelligence would be obtained from "whatever sources available," making no mention of the responsibility of either department.

The Collection Plans

No evidence establishes more conclusively the vast sweep of the Army's surveillance than the documents which listed the items of information that agents were directed to collect. Numerous collection plans are in existence. Three were examined by the Senate subcommittee, the most comprehensive of which was the Intelligence Command's elaboration of the Army-wide plan of April 23, 1969.

The USAINTC Plan followed already-detailed orders and

analyses previously issued by the Army. Former intelligence agents who testified before the Senate subcommittee characterized the whole CONUS intelligence system as a beast which, once set in motion, was infected by the familiar disease of bureaucratic aggrandizement. The plan formulated by the Intelligence Command, however, went far beyond anything ever suggested in Army instructions. The plan, for the most part, is based on the same assumptions as previous ones: The NAACP and CORE are accused of attempting to create, promote, prolong, or aggravate racial tensions; conspiracies lie behind civil disorders; domestic policies are controlled by foreign agencies, leading to the tiresome question, "Is this group financed by Moscow or Peking?"

Collection requirements are always expressed in the vaguest possible language and cover the broadest possible terrain. For example, one item listed under "Anti-War/Anti-Draft Activities" calls for agents to collect information on "minority, racist, terrorist, left-wing, right-wing, and/or other dissident organizations of *possible* future intelligence interest which *may* be *potentially* detrimental to national defense or public order, *not cited by the Attorney General* [italics ours].

Thus agents in the field were left to decide which organizations entertained, *or might entertain, aims* that *could* be detrimental to *what they regarded* as the national defense, public order, or the best interests of the United States.

The same dragnet approach was applied to information pertaining to "militant organizations." The term is undefined. Information on nonmilitant groups is requested when they join militant organizations in sponsoring "demonstrations, rallies or other disturbances. . . . Reporting should include all available information concerning relations with other extremist groups. . . . Reports [on training] should include, insorfar as possible, a breakdown of the topics involved with instruction and a brief description of the subject matter discussed."

Servicemen who were considered "extremist" were subject to intensive surveillance. No distinctions are drawn, however, between those who engage in abstract discussions of remote possibilities and those who advocate immediate participation in criminal acts. Once a soldier is labeled an "extremist," data is collected on him, including his home of record, the day he gets out of the service, and his destination on departure. The fact that the plan singled out these three items for a special listing suggests that the Army intended to alert civilian law enforcement authorities to the suspect's homecoming.

By far the most sweeping category is the one entitled "Demonstrations, Rallies, Marches, Conventions, Conferences and Picketing Activities." The plan calls for details about participating organizations, the important individuals involved, transportation arrangements, and plans for housing the visiting demonstrators or groups. The emphasis throughout the document is certainly not on information about crowds that might be useful to troops charged with clearing streets or enforcing curfews. The emphasis is clearly on identifying individuals and organizations.

The Intelligence Command's Information Collection Plan concluded with "a partial list of organizations . . . of intelligence interest." These included the American Friends Service Committee (Quakers), CORE, the NAACP, Southern Christian Leadership Conference (Dr. Martin Luther King's group), Women's Strike for Peace, and the Interfaith Peace Mission. Why these groups and not others were singled out for Army surveillance is not explained anywhere in the document.

From studying the documents, a number of specifics about the Army's methods become clear. The sweep of the intelligence operations was uninhibited. No distinction was made between those who advocate or practice violence and those who do not. No effort was made to limit the surveillance to massive demonstrations or serious racial flare-ups. Any organization or individual who exercised the constitutional right to criticize the established order automatically was marked for monitoring.

The documents demonstrate how badly the Army misconstrued the purposes of its own surveillance. The extensive facts it col-

lected about numerous civil rights and antiwar organizations did
nothing to change the Army's basic preoccupation with and belief
in the existence of Communist-style conspiracies everywhere.
Undefined terms such as "subversive," "militant," "extremist," and "dissident" were made to substitute for careful
analysis, while the statutory and historical bases for the civil
disturbance mission appear to have been ignored altogether.

The Army also totally misconceived its own intelligence needs.
The main job of riot troops has always been to clear the streets of
mobs, protect property, and enforce curfews. This "clear and
hold" mission has always been emphasized and the possibility that
troops may also have to detain persons who commit criminal acts
in their presence has always been deemphasized. The collection
plans seem to have the assignment backwards. No tactical
information—road construction, detours, obstructions, etc.—was
processed, only the information necessary to identify dissenters.
The task force commander, for whom this information was supposedly being collected, is really the forgotten man in the whole
scheme of things.

Lastly, it is rather disturbing to realize that documents such as
this could circulate throughout the government without eliciting a
whimper of protest anywhere from anyone. Thousands of uniformed and civilian officials who received copies of the various
collection plans, as far as we can assess, never questioned the
impact of such a plan on civil-military relations, the liberties of
citizens, or the health of the body politic.

Whether these officials were intimidated by the documents'
"CONFIDENTIAL" stamp, unwilling to question another
agency's practices, or oblivious to the possible dangers, we do not
know. We do know that a free society demands greater vigilance
than these men showed.

Methods, Reporting, and Dissemination

The Army obtained much of its information about civilian
politics without resort to covert means. Liaison with municipal,

state, and campus police, and access to the files of the Federal Bureau of Investigation, provided the bulk of the information used in reports on individuals and organizations. In addition, Army intelligence units culled hundreds of national, community, campus and "underground" newspapers and magazines, as well as the major wire services, for information on incidents, planned demonstrations, personalities, and organizations. In some instances, subscriptions were taken out under aliases with "mail drop" addresses. CIAB, for example, subscribed to some publications in the name of "R. Allen Lee Associates, Box 922, Alexandria, Virginia 22333."

Direct agent observation of rallies, demonstrations, and marches furnished untold thousands of reports. In most instances, the agents simply watched, acting as any participant or spectator would.

An undetermined fraction of its information, however, was obtained from covert operations where identities and affiliations of the agents were deliberately concealed through the use of bogus identification, cover stories, or other deceits. Investigation has confirmed that, among other assignments, Army agents:

—Infiltrated a number of civilian organizations which had no connection whatsoever with the Armed Forces.

—Attended both the Republican and Democratic National Conventions in 1968.

—Posed as press photographers and newsmen, often with bogus credentials.

—Infiltrated the 1968 Poor People's Campaign and Resurrection City.

—Rode buses and trains carrying demonstrators to the 1967 March on the Pentagon.

—Infiltrated a Yippie Commune in Washington, D.C., during the 1969 Counterinaugural. The use of marijuana and liquor at government expense was authorized for this operation.

—Posed as television newsmen interviewing demonstrators in Atlanta, Chicago, Washington, D.C., and Catonsville, Maryland.

—Were arrested at Howard University while participating in a rock-throwing crowd.

Without revealing the details of any prescribed *modus operandi*, these examples suggest ways in which Army intelligence conducted its domestic intelligence operations.

The extent to which these covert operations were actually authorized by the Department of the Army and the commanding generals of both collection agencies is not very clear. According to present Defense Department officials, their predecessors demanded reams of information from Army intelligence, but did not question how that information was collected.

Former analysts also report that the information they received from the field was "sanitized" before it was passed on to the Under Secretary and the General Counsel. In this way the sources of the material were effectively concealed from the civilian superiors in the executive branch. The full extent of the Pentagon's knowledge of these operations, as well as their exact nature and justification, is unknown because the Pentagon has persistently refused to declassify its records. If ever subpoenaed, they would probably be conveniently "lost."

Army intelligence reported and disseminated the information it collected with the zeal of a competitive wire service. Indeed, former agents of the Intelligence Command recall Brigadier General William H. Blakefield's exhortation to "beat the AP."

Of all the methods of communication, the teletype network installed during 1966 and 1967 was probably the most important. It eventually linked the Intelligence Command's headquarters with every MI office which included a CONUS intelligence section. Telephone hot lines, radios, and videotape camera equipment rounded out the Army's arsenal of major communications equipment.

The formats of most of the intelligence reports were the same as those developed during World War II. Most common was the "spot report," a cryptic six-paragraph or fourteen-paragraph report normally used to describe incidents. When these were based on direct agent observation of demonstrations, more detailed "agent reports" (ARs) often followed. These were modeled on the standard format used to describe the results of personnel security investigations. These reports later provided many of the details used to prepare "characterizations" of individuals and groups. Spot reports and ARs were condensed at various command levels for inclusion in daily, weekly, and monthly intelligence summaries.

The precise format of CONUS intelligence reports is less significant than the fact that most of them had been in continuous use since the 1940s. Their existence provides further confirmation that the surveillance of the late 1960s was not an aberration.

One of the most disturbing aspects of the reporting system operated by the Intelligence Command was the indiscriminate dissemination of many of its reports. No effort was ever made to limit the distribution of spot reports and intelligence summaries to units with a genuine "need to know." On the contrary, reports of the most minor, lawful demonstrations within the United States were regularly flashed to Army headquarters in Europe, Hawaii, Alaska, and Panama. Volume, not utility, was the criterion by which the program was judged. By 1969, the USAINTC teletype was transmitting an average of 1,200 spot reports per month.

Nature of Processed Intelligence

For the most part, the Army's domestic intelligence machine worked like a giant vacuum cleaner which indiscriminately pulled in any information even remotely related to political activism. Vast amounts of raw intelligence were pumped through the system and dumped onto potential users—unsorted, unchecked, and unevaluated. The sheer volume alone prevented thoughtful analysis.

Those agencies or commands which were charged to analyze

intelligence often did not even have formal guidelines of any sort to assist them. Even if they did, they rarely had the skilled manpower necessary to perform such analyses. The CIAB's domestic section, which supplied the bulk of information for the Army's decision-makers, was staffed by "analysts" with little education or experience in the field. In 1968 these included a tank commander with a B.S. in chemistry, an infantry officer from West Point, a college dropout, several former counterespionage agents who had spent most of their adult lives overseas, and a lawyer with no background in civil liberties.

Not surprisingly, the analyses took the form of simple, raw compilations of data. Of these, two are particularly significant: the Intelligence Command's "blacklist" and the CIAB's compendium.

Blacklist

The blacklist was a six-volume mugbook published by the Intelligence Command. Its formal title was *Individuals Active in Civil Disturbances*, and it included profiles of over 1,000 individuals. Each page contained three entries, consisting of a photograph (on the left) and descriptive data, including name, birthdate, address, occupation, arrest record, organizational affiliation, associations, and miscellaneous information. Each volume pertained to a particular geographical area.

Although the arrest records of many individuals were detailed, no place had been left to note the dispositions of any of these cases. Many individuals included in the volumes appear to have had no arrest records at all. Of the 223 entries in Volume 2, 52 showed no record of arrest. Of those with arrest records, many appeared to have been arrested only once, typically for participating in a civil rights demonstration. In Volume 3, 94 of the 237 persons profiled were young black citizens with no distinction other than that they were members of groups arrested for either parading without a permit in Lee County, Alabama, on September 1, 1965, or committing an unidentified crime in Tuscaloosa, Alabama. Only a few of the entries in any of the volumes note felony arrests (kidnapping, burglary, grand larceny, auto theft). Most entries are for unlawful assembly, breach of the peace, trespassing, using obscene language, and the like.

Short notations commented on the individual's political beliefs, actions, or associations. One person had "numerous pro-Communist associates." Another, a young black male with no arrest record, was described nevertheless as an "extremely radical, militant individual." Other notable characterizations included "Avowed Marxist," "reported to be psycho," "Black Power advocate," "wants to abolish the House Un-American Activities Committee," "active demonstrator, has Red background, is a radical," and "paranoid trends, not qualified for military services."

One of the more striking, if absurd, references in the description of a nationally known civil rights leader was the entry under "Associates": "Known to have many known associates."

On the basis of the information set forth in these mug books, it is clear that numerous citizens were marked as subjects of Army intelligence interest on the basis of wholly lawful political behavior or minor infractions of local law stemming from civil rights activities. The activities of many of these persons were so innocuous that it is impossible to determine why they would be included in a publication presumably compiled to assist Army commanders in their efforts to quell civil disturbances.

What purpose these books were really supposed to serve has never been explained. Shortly after their existence was disclosed in January 1970, the Department of the Army ordered them destroyed. The Army general counsel admitted in a letter to Senator Sam Ervin that they were totally unnecessary to the Army's civil disturbance mission, but didn't explain why they had been compiled. Whether the Army carried out its orders, as we shall see in other cases, is not something which can simply be assumed.

Compendium

The second important domestic intelligence compilation was a set of two yellow, vinyl-covered looseleaf binders popularly known as the "compendium." Both volumes, classified as SECRET, were entitled "Civil Disturbances and Dissidence." Volume 1 concerned *Cities and Organizations of Interest*; Volume 2, *Personalities of Interest*. Both volumes bore the imprint of "Headquarters, Department of the Army; Office of the Assistant Chief of Staff for Intelligence" and opened with the acknowledgment, "The basic information on organizations and individuals contained herein has been provided primarily by the Federal Bureau of Investigation."

City summaries in Volume 1 averaged approximately one page each and included "Basic Data" such as population, ethnic composition and unemployment rate as well as "Significant Organizational Activity," which described those organizations thought to have the greatest bearing on future disturbances. What kind of bearing usually was not considered or indicated. "Potential Trouble Areas" cited in the summaries were invariably black neighborhoods.

Characterizations of groups were presented in capsule form, usually without evidence to back up such designations as "Communist" or "antiwhite." The majority of organizations mentioned were black, including the NAACP, CORE, SCLC, and Student Non-Violent Coordinating Committee. The Students for a Democratic Society, Southern Students Organizing Committee, and some chapters of the Ku Klux Klan were also sprinkled in. What kind of influence they had in past disturbances or were expected to have in future ones was rarely mentioned.

"Organizations of Interest" are broken down into four categories: political, racial, antiwar/antidraft, and international. The preface to Part II states, "a few of the organizations represented in this compendium are entirely legitimate and legal [in their] aims and aspirations." The NAACP and the Urban League fall into this group, despite the fact that the NAACP was still characterized by the Intelligence Command as an organization attempting "to create, prolong, promote or aggravate racial tensions."

Over one hundred organizations were described, usually in one or two pages each. Many of them were extremely small and strictly local in nature. Subversive influences were detailed, but never with documentary evidence to prove the vague generalities. "There is no evidence of infiltration or influence by a subversive element" in the American Friends Service Committee, as far as the Army is concerned, but CORE was reportedly "influenced and infiltrated by members of Communist front groups." From the looks of it, most of the information included could have easily been obtained from the news media or from the groups' own publications.

Volume 2 of the compendium contained biographical sketches on 345 "personalities of interest," 243 of them active on the domestic political scene, 102 active in foreign countries. Most sketches were less than a page long and stressed "Political/Organizational Affiliation and Activity." Some individuals, not aligned with any organization, were evidently included merely because they were outspoken on racial or antiwar issues.

The contents of the sketches varied from brief notes on the individual's organizational roles to elaborate disclosures of his mental stability, family situation, schooling, occupation, financial condition, criminal record, political associations, and views (as evidenced by his speeches and statements). Some of the entries indicated that the confidentiality of military medical records had been violated. Other entries suggested that the FBI or the Army obtained the results of examinations by private physicians or psychiatrists.

How some of the people merited inclusion is a mystery. The chairman and vice-chairman of one southwestern community's Committee to End the War in Vietnam are included in the volume, while some well-known antiwar personalities, including some of the defendants in the Chicago Eight conspiracy trial, were never mentioned.

The chief criteria for selection appeared to have been involvement in racially oriented orgaizations. Of the 243 persons in the domestic section, 193 were active in either supporting or opposing increased minority rights. All but a few of the rest were associated with the antiwar movement.

The compendium was ordered destroyed in March 1970, shortly after its existence was exposed by the Chicago *Sun-Times*. Three hundred and forty-eight copies of Volume 1 and 346 copies of Volume 2 had been distributed. Copies went to the Defense Department, State Department, FBI, CIA, Justice Department, the Secret Service, NASA, and eight defense attachés in U.S. embassies overseas, including Canada, West Germany, and the Soviet Union. The compendium was available to thousands of officials. Strange though it may seem, no one ever lodged an official protest against the invasion of privacy, the usurpation of authority, or the vast waste of money that the compendium represented.

Storage of Intelligence Data

As we have seen, the Army's records on civilian political activity were voluminous and far-reaching. Scores of local, regional, and national record centers kept track of individuals and organizations from Unitarian church groups to the Ku Klux Klan. Computers were generally used to store the information and to index libraries of dossiers. Where computers proved unnecessary, card indexes were used to catalogue the information. The records were spread throughout the nation in a number of separate storage areas, most of which still exist. We will attempt a short summary of the storage plans and locations.

Subversives File

The oldest of the files was the subversives search file, a collection of dossiers on persons and organizations considered a threat to national security. Yet the contents of this dossier collection exceeded the scope suggested by its own definition of purpose: threats to national security. Until 1971, the subjects included public officials, among them congressmen and governors, and such subversive organizations as the American Friends Service Committee, the NAACP and Women's Strike for Peace.

These records were kept in a huge sheet-metal warehouse at Fort Holabird, Maryland, along with the rest of the intelligence data collected by the Intelligence Command. Along with the four other satellite files to follow in this description, it is part of the Investigatory Records Repository, the most extensive system of files maintained by the Army. Most of the information is duplicated by the FBI.

The subversives file contains somewhere in the neighborhood of 250,000 dossiers.

Incident Data Files

Records of incidents of interest to military intelligence were filed in both noncomputerized and computerized form at Fort Holabird.

The computerization of the ''spot reports'' and ''agent reports'' filed by investigators in the field reflected an attempt to collect the information and plot trends and discern incipient civil disorders.

For each person and organization listed in the file there was an index number. Reference to this number would permit the analyst to produce lists of members of particular organizations and lists of organizations to which specified persons belonged. The Intelligence Command could also produce a list of all incidents involving an organization.

The fate of these files remains in doubt. Despite directives to destroy them and two series of inspections, the Senate Subcommittee has received unconfirmed reports that the non-computerized spot reports have not been destroyed. Orders to destroy the computer bank were issued on February 19, 1970. This destruction could not be verified by the Subcommittee.

Biographical Data File

The biographical data file contained approximately ten entries per page. Subcommittee staff members estimated that at least 4,000 persons were listed. Some of the codes used in the computer print-outs were curious: Target, Ideology, and Derogatory Information, for instance. The Army insisted that all instruction books had been destroyed, and they were unable to find anyone with personal knowledge of the "meaning" of these terms as they applied to the various individuals. Two code books—one for the biographical file, the other for the incident file—mysteriously turned up after the denials.

Most of the categories—occupation, country, organization, etc.—were designated by digital codes whose meanings were not at all evident from the print-out. Without the missing code book that was finally turned up, it would have been impossible to interpret the data.

Once "translated," however, the file began to take on a pretty sinister form. According to the code book, for example, there were 250 possible occupational designations, ranging from B-girl to clamdigger, armament specialist to symphony conductor. The "ideology" section listed 13 possible codes, signifying Communist-inclined, anti-United States, moderate, pro-Castro, ultranationalist, among others.

The organization list was the most revealing of all. It listed no less than 770 groups, including the *National Review*, the League of Women Voters, the Urban League, Young Democrats, Double Sex Kings, Bay Area Festival Committee, and the International Longshoremen's and Warehousemen's Union, among other obviously subversive and highly dangerous groups of high school students, churches and government committeemen. Given the fact that the code book was established at the time the computer system was established, it indicates how comprehensive the Fort Holabird computer system was intended to be. Apparently the Army had prepared a list of politically suspect organizations before it even collected any information on which to base such a list.

Local Files

Fort Holabird was not the only repository for the Intelligence Command's files on civilians. Duplicates of virtually every report there existed elsewhere among the more than 300 stateside offices of the Command. Copies were often distributed, often indiscriminately, throughout the system and went into other data banks. Some were swapped with municipal intelligence squads, state police, the National Guard, FBI, CIA, the Navy, the Air Force, and other federal and state agencies.

The files maintained by subordinate Intelligence Command offices were often extensive. A former agent of the Minneapolis-St. Paul office recalls the destruction of "a good fifty pounds" of files near the beginning of 1971. They had been hidden away in violation of the June 1970 destruction order.

No one can really be sure that some of these files do not still exist. Six months after the incident file was ordered destroyed, it was discovered that the entire data bank could be reconstituted. Three months after that, an "inactive" tape was discovered. Destruction has been far from assured.

The extent of the Intelligence Command's files are disturbing in themselves. They represent only a portion of the Army's holdings.

CONARC—Incident File

Like the Intelligence Command, the Continental Army Command maintained a nationwide network of computerized and non-computerized files on civilians. For nine months after the original Senate correspondence with the Army had begun, the Army still acknowledged only the data bank at Fort Holabird. It wasn't until November 27, 1970, that CONARC's computers were admitted to. Even then, in a short announcement from Undersecretary Beal, no mention was made of their origins, contents, scope, purposes, or use.

Only after the Senate hearings had concluded did the facts on CONARC's participation in the surveillance come out. Like the Intelligence Command, the subcommittee learned, CONARC had turned to computers in the late 1960s. The Fort Monroe data bank, known as CRIS (Counterintelligence Records Intelligence System), was established in January 1968 and computerized in May. Similar to the organization of other collections, the CRIS computer had three components: a personality file, an incident file, and an organization file with "cross-rference retrieval capability."

The incident bank was built mainly on spot reports and appears to have been part of an ambitious, independent, but unsophisticated effort by CONARC to predict civil disorders through the statistical analysis of "indicators," such as crime rates, regularity of false alarms, etc. Importantly, each incident entry included a list of all individuals and organizations involved. Given the "retrieval capability" of the system, this meant that all reports which mentioned someone only incidentally could be easily reassembled if that person later became a "personality of interest."

The five volumes of the "personalities edition" contain 2,269 pages of detailed summaries of the political beliefs and activities of nearly 5,500 persons, along with a ninety-nine-page index. The categories, seventeen of them, which were filled out on each person were sufficiently vague to allow the agent ample latitude for independent judgment. He was supposed to judge a person's militancy, or lack of it, how much he supported a particular organization, his "leadership effectiveness," and other hard-to-evaluate characterizations. As we have come to expect, there is little indication that the file would have been of much use for the occurrences—civil disturbances, etc.—which had supposedly necessitated its existence. No restrictions were placed on dissemination of the information.

The continental commands subordinate to CONARC also managed to pile up a bunch of information on people. Between them, the First, Third, Fourth, Fifth, and Sixth Armies, and the Military District of Washington, maintained approximately 455 linear feet of cards and dossiers on personalities and organizations. This is the equivalent of about fifty-seven four-drawer file cabinets.

CIAB

The task of CONARC and USAINTC was to report and store as much data as possible. Speed and volume were the criteria by which their performances were evaluated. Thus, where they could, they turned to computers.

The Counterintelligence Analysis Branch (CIAB) was a different kind of agency, concerned with producing analyses of matters of counterintelligence importance occurring anywhere in the world. To facilitate their job, they kept a large microfilm archive called the "Counterintelligence Reference File System." By early 1970, the archive contained approximately 117,500 documents, of which half or more related to civilian political activity. The index to these documents (which *was* computerized) contained 189,000 entries identifying types of activities and references to 113,250 organizational and 152,000 personality entries. Estimates of how much of this was solely in the realm of domestic civilian politics are difficult to come up with. One agent mentioned that the computer print-out of the domestic portion of the index was a foot and a half to two feet thick. That's a pretty good estimate.

The CIAB files included such personalities as Dr. Martin Luther King, Conrad Lynn, the Reverend Jesse Jackson, Joan Baez, Arlo Guthrie, Arlo Tatum, and Whitney Young. Reports on these individuals frequently detailed travels, education, and schooling, and even contained information on their families as well.

There were other data banks. There were thousands of other files, divided among local offices and other agencies within the Army hierarchy. Listing them would take many more pages but would not really change the basic conclusions.

The Army conducted surveillance of American citizens with little authorization—"weak" is the word—and less care. Their admissions have come slowly and grudgingly. The first disclosures that a computer on civilian political activity even existed in the Pentagon's domestic war room had to come from the New York *Times* on July 4, 1971. The cover-up has been messy. Not all of the facts have emerged, or possibly ever will.

What had taken place was not so much a conscious effort to subvert the freedoms of speech and association, as it was a classic example of a burgeoning bureaucracy going out of control, with no direction and no limitations. What began as a limited intelligence activity by individual commands responding to the military's limited need for information for use during civil disturbances mushroomed into an elaborate nationwide system with the potential to monitor any and all political expression. No person or organization was too insignificant to monitor; no activity or incident too irrelevant to record. Yet by their own admission, the responsible appointees of the Johnson and Nixon administrations were unaware even of the existence of the data banks until 1970.

How could such a program get out of hand? It is probably because there were too many people with too little to do and yet with vast untapped resources at their disposal. Thousands of Army intelligence agents, trained for surveillance work, but with little opportunity to put it into practice, were loosed by their superiors on the American public. The gauge of success was the quantity of information recorded. And the myriad of Army intelligence computers were more than competent receptacles for all that the agents could transcribe.

It is not a particularly difficult phenomenon to understand. Military intelligence officers whose careers were dependent upon performing were naturally disposed to do too much rather than too little. For them, surveillance of citizens was a matter of doing their job—a matter of operational efficiency. Sensitivity to individual liberties was not an "operative" concern.

Army surveillance, we are assured, has now been curtailed. Yet, as Congressman Ed Koch remarked, "If the Army says they don't have these files any more they're probably telling the truth—it may be they destroyed one list and just transferred the information to another. That's the nature of the government. They're like squirrels."

The case of the Army is not unique, however; it does not represent the only recorded case study of bureaucratic insensitivity to individual liberties. The modern bureaucracy often places expediency—whether wittingly or not—above any concern for individual liberties. Even those segments of the bureaucracy which do have a valid justification for collecting personal information from the people are prone to go beyond their legitimate needs. Computerization has made such excesses tempting. Despite the objectives of the bureaucrat, we cannot but feel that in his collecting, cataloguing, and storing of personal information, there are the seeds of repression.

The Orwellian nightmare of a government always watching and, armed with the knowledge of its citizens' thoughts and ambitions, silencing their adverse views with real or presumed threats of reprisals, is a vision which has haunted twentieth-century man since it was conceived. Yet those charged with the operation of government continue to ignore the warning. Army intelligence collected the most personal of information for preservation in its computers. It was not unusual to find in the Army's files details of one's memberships, associates, remarks, published statements, attendance at meetings, personal finances, sexual activities, arrests, and personality quirks preserved in perpetuity. Such excesses cannot be tolerated in a free society.

After all, the loss of anonymity occasioned by having an opinion or an association recorded, creates a climate of subtle coercion. No longer could a man march down Pennsylvania Avenue with his sign and return innocently to his hometown, his identity forgotten. No longer would the memory of the author of a political article fade as the pages of his rhetoric yellow and crumble with time. No longer would the flamboyant words exchanged in debate lose their relevance with the issue of the moment that prompted them.

The effect would make it impossible for a man to forget any part of his past. He could not start over again. In fact, he might be more inclined never to begin at all. The lower road of silence, unproductive but less fraught with danger, may become the more appetizing alternative. It is a prospect that must be shunned.

Chapter Ten:

At This Point in Time: Watergate

"I don't believe in predictin' I'm gonna knock a man out, because if you tell me you're gonna push me out that window at 12 o'clock tonight, I'm gonna sit there and watch you along about 11:59."—Joe Frazier, in a Playboy *interview.*

At first there was only a trickle of stagnant water that escaped from the crack in the dam. And then little by little the crack grew until the trickle became a raging river. The impenetrable structure that once was our executive branch of government shook and shuddered with the roar of the Watergate revelations. Everyone, or almost everyone; there are some known exceptions—wants to get rid of all that ill-smelling water, no matter who gets swept away in the powerful current, but one nagging doubt still bothers many people. Will the whole dam be swept away in the process? Or will the essential structure hold? How did it happen anyway? Where was the little Dutch boy with his proverbial finger?

The event, in the words of some of those intimately involved, started like this:

Richard M. Nixon, August 29, 1972: "[Mr. Dean's] investigation indicates that no one in this administration, presently employed, was involved in this bizarre incident. . . . What really hurts in matters of this sort is not the fact that they occur, because overzealous people in campaigns do things that are wrong. What really hurts is if you try to cover it up.''

Jeb Stuart Magruder, June 25, 1973: ''I think there was no question that the cover-up began that Saturday when we realized there was a break-in. I do not think there was ever any discussion that there would not be a cover-up.''

John Dean, June 25, 1973: ''I had no advance knowledge that the President was going to indicate that I had investigated the matter and found no complicity on the part of anybody at the White House or anyone presently employed in the Administration. I first learned of . . . it on a television news broadcast.''

H. R. Haldeman, July 30, 1973: ''I had no personal motivation to cover up anything because I had no personal involvement and I knew the President had no involvement. I understand and believed that no one else in the White House was involved in the Watergate planning and break-in, and I still understand and believe that. It was obvious that some people at the Committee [to Re-Elect the President] were involved, but I had no idea who, or how far up, and I still don't—because I don't know now whom to believe.''

L. Patrick Gray, August 6, 1973: ''I said early in the game that I thought that Watergate would be a spreading stain that would tarnish everyone with whom it came in contact and I am no exception. I had a responsibility . . . not to permit myself to be used, not to permit myself to be deceived, and I failed in that responsibility and I have never failed in anything that I have undertaken until this point in time. It hurts.''

It not only hurts Mr. Gray—ex-director of the FBI—it hurts all of us. It has hurt the bricklayer and the farmer as much as the men on Wall Street and the bemedaled generals in the Pentagon. It is Watergate, the most publicized government scandal in the history of the United States.

Watergate, the building complex from which the scandal got its name, is a $78-million, six-year-old five-building cluster of ostentatious high-rise apartment, office, and hotel units that rises from the banks of the Potomac River like a concrete sculpture, only three-quarters completed. It is a Nixon Era colosseum.

The Watergate stands on the old Washington Gas Works property in Foggy Bottom, its toothy balconies and opulent furnishings in stark contrast to its spartan-looking next-door neighbor, the John F. Kennedy Center for the Performing Arts. It is home for 1,500 Washingtonians, but only the affluent can afford its four swimming pools, two restaurants, private waterfall, and royal prices. Among its inmates are a dozen senators and representatives; the Postmaster General; two Cabinet members; the Treasurer of the United States; the directors of the Census, the Mint, the Voice of America, and the Agency for International Development; a score of ambassadors, judges, and agency chiefs; and several millionaires.

On the seventh floor, Martha Mitchell once wreaked havoc by telephone. On the fourteenth, President Nixon's longtime personal secretary, Rose Mary Woods, owned a lavish penthouse. On the sixth floor, on June 17, 1972, police caught five incompetent burglars attempting to bug the Democratic National Committee Headquarters on the orders of officials at the Committee to Re-Elect the President.

The Watergate was famous overnight. Sightseers added it to their list of must-sees right after the Washington Monument and the Lincoln Memorial. Republicans cringed at the very mention of the word. Democrats were secretly overjoyed. But not for long, for soon they too began to feel the awesome reverberations that the simple bugging operation would bring.

By now, many of the facts—complex, disturbing, contradictory—have been pulled out of both reluctant and eager witnesses. The scandal sent President Nixon to an early retirement. Richard Milhous Nixon, the archetypal loser of American politics, transformed by the events of the 1972 Presidential campaign into the biggest winner in history, was a loser again, less than two years after his monumental "mandate." Thirty-seven days of testimony, which filled more than 7,000 typewritten pages, had begun to slowly seal the fate of Nixon's future.

It was suddenly clear, all of the misleading and contradictory testimony notwithstanding, that administration denials of responsibility for the break-in were lies. How high up this responsibility reached—whether or not it reached right into the Oval Office —may never be perfectly clear. But as Nixon himself once stated in a speech addressed to the nation, "I am responsible." And that "I" is not only the President, but all of us. And once this is over, we should try to make sure it never happens again.

Of course, to paraphrase Joe Frazier's quote at the beginning of this chapter, no one told us they were going to push us out the window at twelve o'clock, so we weren't watching.

The Nixon Administration, and its political apparatus, the Committee to Re-Elect the President, began by disavowing any connection with the five men arrested that June, but when connections began to appear, that official line was amended to read that no one in "senior status" at the committee or in the White House was involved. Next, President Nixon amended the statement to read that no one "presently employed" was a participant.

Once the numerous cats began jumping out of their bags, all previous statements became inoperative. The President tried everything in his considerable power to stem the flow of mutinous aides who were selling their loyalty for immunity, because there was evidently still too much to conceal. The underlying assumption, all too obvious, was the President's personal involvement with the seamy side of his Administration and reelection. Nixon, in the past, was never a preoccupied, innocent, and naive victim of aides who were a trifle too overzealous. The history of Nixon in public life is one of dirty tricks in politics. His style inspired the men around him. Watergate was not a single, contained scandal, as the President would like us to believe; it is a symptom of the way he plays the game—and the object of the game is to win.

Seven men were originally indicted for the Watergate break-in;

indictment of many more who participated in the various aspects of the whole picture is either a fact or expected before the play is done. Their defenses were completely in line with the type of mentality that allowed them to participate in the first place. For instance, a defense lawyer at the trial of James McCord, Jr., in January 1972 said that his client had a legal right to participate in the raid on Democratic National Headquarters because he feared "violence to law officials and Republican officials including the President himself."

Gerald Alch, McCord's attorney, called this logic the "doctrine of duress argument," which he said provided that "if a man has a reasonable belief to anticipate violence to himself and to others, he has a legal right to break the law" to prevent greater harm. Alch never stated from whom this violence was expected or what form McCord expected it to take, or who is to determine what is a "reasonable belief."

Other participants shied away from such legalistic doctrines and tried to equate the Watergate affair with the long tradition of political dirty tricks almost as old as the concept of voting. It's certainly true that a lot of unsavory events have occurred time and again in various campaigns—stealing official stationery to issue phony press releases, publishing embarrassing out-of-context photographs, and leaking dubious information at the right time to the right people for maximum effect, have become depressingly common tactics over the years.

Some of the "good old dirty tricks" are more funny than dirty, and although in the range of the practical jokester that nobody really likes, seemingly harmless. A saboteur loosed a box of live cockroaches in Republican headquarters in Manhattan. Aides for LBJ poured itching powder down the backs of demonstrators at political rallies. No one can carry a sign with much dignity with such an overwhelming desire to scratch. The line, though, between funny and dirty sometimes begins to blur, as in the case of that trick played on Les Marshall, a Democrat running for a Council seat in New Castle County, Pennsylvania, in 1966.

Someone sent a truck urging citizens to "Vote For Marshall" into a conservative white ethnic neighborhood. The truck and the sign did him no harm; it was the all-black band—complete with scantily clad go-go girls—who rode the truck, that raised the conservative eyebrows. Marshall lost the election. Was this the reason? Probably not, but it certainly didn't win him any votes, and it may have lost him some.

The alltime champion of political prankinsteins is Democratic politician Dick Tuck, who was remarkably quiet in 1972. Maybe he felt he couldn't compete with the professionals who were working for the other side.

Tuck's best-known pranks have always been at the expense of Richard Nixon, who was more than a little surprised to open a Chinese fortune cookie and find a slip of paper that read "Kennedy will win" during the 1960 Presidential campaign. Nixon was even a little angry when, during his 1962 campaign for Governor of California, his campaign train jerked into life in the middle of one of his speeches. Tuck, donning a railman's cap, had signaled the engineer of the campaign train to pull out. Still funny? To most people it was.

That kind of fun and games is as similar to the Watergate fiasco, however, as the Cookie Monster is to Frankenstein's Monster. Yet John Ehrlichman tried to equate the two in a statement four months after the break-in. Not everyone saw it that way.

George McGovern said rather sarcastically, "He [Ehrlichman] said that hiring a network of more than fifty political operatives to forge letters, to impersonate officials of various Democratic campaigns, to incite political riots at our political rallies, to issue phony press releases in the names of others—in this case in the name of Democratic campaigners—to withhold evidence from a grand jury, to illegally enter the offices of the opposition party, to steal private files and to unlawfully wiretap private conversations of Democratic officials—he said all these things are just political pranks that we've always had in America."

Of course George McGovern is not as objective about the whole thing as some other people might be, but he makes an obvious point.

So far the reputation to benefit most from the whole affair (anyone who was in any way touched by the Watergate smell) seems to have been that of the late J. Edgar Hoover. Everyone —liberal columnists, conservative editorialists, and Senator Sam Ervin—has ultimately reached the same conclusion. If J. Edgar Hoover's advice had been heeded, there would have been no plumbers to "plug White House leaks," no break-ins—in fact, no Watergate.

A lot of strange events have led to this equally perplexing picture of Hoover as a lone bastion, staunchly protecting the civil rights of the American people. The story begins in 1970.

The White House, it seems, wanted to bring back those free-wheeling days of yore, before 1966, when FBI "black bag jobs" (illegal entry and burglary of homes and offices) and expanded use of electronic surveillance against "political subversives" were the order of the day.

The administration was having a running battle with Hoover over the role of the FBI. The administration officials wanted the Bureau to forget the common criminals and Old Left rev-olutionaries for a while and concentrate on the New Left political organizations and black nationalist groups. Nixon asked Hoover early in 1970 if foreign countries were behind the radical political conspiracy in the United States. The Bureau couldn't answer.

In June 1970, Nixon decided it was time to upgrade domestic intelligence-gathering techniques. He brought together the direc-tors of the FBI, CIA, NSA (National Security Agency), DIA (Defense Intelligence Agency), and each of the military services, instructing them to work out a plan for increased surveillance.

Tom Charles Huston, a lower-echelon White House aide, was Nixon's personal liaison. From this meeting, and subsequent events, came two memos. One, titled "Domestic Intelligence Gathering Plan: Recommendations," was the interagency committee's report; a memo from Tom Charles Huston to the

White House chief of staff, H. R. Haldeman, was issued in July, 1970. Both were classified "Top Secret."

Nixon's "decision memorandum," dated July 15, 1970, went along with every recommendation the committee had made. Specifically, the Nixon decision was:

(a) The National Security Agency should be permitted "to program for coverage and communications of U.S. citizens using international facilities."

(b) "to intensify coverage [electronic surveillance and penetrations] of individuals and groups in the United States who pose a major threat to the internal security. Also coverage of foreign nationals and diplomatic establishments in the United States . . . is to be intensified."

(c) "Restrictions on legal [mail] coverage are to be removed, restrictions on covert [mail] coverage are to be relaxed . . ."

(The committee's report had remarked that "covert coverage is illegal . . . [but] the advantages to be derived from its use outweighs the risks." The only valid argument against legal mail covers, the committee noted, was that "civil liberties people may become upset.")

(d) "Restraints on the use of surreptitious entry are to be removed."

(As the committee blandly stated in its recommendations, "use of this technique is clearly illegal; it amounts to burglary. It is also highly risky and could result in great embarrassment if exposed. However, it is also the most fruitful tool and can produce the type of intelligence which cannot be obtained in any other fashion.")

(e) "Coverage of violence-prone campus and student related groups is to be increased. All restraints which limit this coverage are to be removed. Also, CIA coverage of American students (and others) travelling or living abroad is to be increased."

(The committee had already decided that possible exposure "is a price we must be willing to pay for effective coverage of the campus scene.")

The Interagency Group on Domestic Intelligence and Internal Security was to become a permanent fixture, chaired by J. Edgar Hoover. Huston was still the White House man on the inside. The plan was to be implemented immediately.

Only Hoover stood in the way. As chairman of the group that had submitted the recommendations which Nixon approved point-by-point, he had detailed in footnotes his objections to virtually every proposal. When Nixon ignored the protests and issued his "decision memorandum," Hoover got on the phone to San Clemente and again informed the President of his disapproval. He used stronger language this time than he had used in the footnotes, and Nixon knuckled under. The entire plan was scrapped five days after it was approved.

Huston, who had called the report a "first-rate job" in his memo to Haldeman, resigned from the White House in 1971 and was appointed to the Census Bureau's Advisory Committee on Privacy and Confidentiality. Which leads one to wonder.

Nixon didn't give up on the plan entirely, however. Since he couldn't have Hoover's cooperation in setting up one national intelligence-gathering apparatus out of the existing agencies, he decided to form his own group. The team of White House snoopers, answerable only to a handful of administration officials, was later to become known as the "plumbers" ostensibly because of their overt assignment to plug up leaks from the White House.

The real mission of the plumbers, one must think now that many of their activities have been made public, was to bludgeon the Bill of Rights. Among other things, E. Howard Hunt and G. Gordon Liddy directed Cuban provocateurs to beat up Daniel Ellsberg, organized the burglary of his psychiatrist's office, and engineered the break-in (twice) of the Democratic party headquarters.

A note on J. Edgar Hoover's role in all this is in order. Hoover comes off as a civil libertarian, without whose opposition the Nixon Administration would have ridden roughshod over the rights of the people in such a way as to make the "horrors" of

Watergate seem like a gentle comedy. Hoover seems to have saved us a great deal. And he probably did. Although his motivation in the opposition to Nixon's "decision" may have been a little less than being a champion of the people.

Hoover, who built his unparalleled empire partly by avoiding Attorney Generals and dealing directly with Presidents, *had* to oppose the Huston memorandum, which proposed an interagency group that would supervise the FBI and possibly stand between the director and his access to the Oval Office. He did this out of his own sense of power politics, it seems logical to assume, not out of some idealistic fervor for citizens' rights. Hoover would, of course, oppose a plan which advocated that "CIA coverage of American students . . . should be increased" because "the FBI does not currently recruit any campus sources among individuals below 21 years of age." (Perhaps as a result of such threats, the minimum age for FBI informers was lowered to eighteen a few months later. J. Edgar never left holes big enough for other agencies to crawl through if he could help it.)

Hoover's power was based on the fact that he had skillfully resisted incursions on the FBI's jurisdiction while simultaneously seizing on the "national security" issue to increase his fiefdom. He had reluctantly lent FBI cooperation to Robert Kennedy's "Get Hoffa" campaign only because he resented any non-FBI men doing any investigations, and if Hoover didn't cooperate, Kennedy would have gotten someone else.

There are a lot of lessons to be drawn from Watergate, but let us not think that one of them is our safety as citizens and that the integrity of our politicians rests on our luck in finding another J. Edgar Hoover to preside over our FBI. His reaction was only that of a bureaucrat trying to keep people (whomever it might be) from weakening his empire.

However, one of the lessons which we feel should be drawn from Watergate is that the press should never be allowed to be intimidated from doing its job. What would have happened if the Nixon Administration's attack on "freedom of the press" had succeeded? Would the ever-tightening web of Nixon's Big Brother government still be growing stronger?

Spiro Agnew's wordy condemnations of what he termed "advocacy journalism" are now legendary. Nattering Nabobs of Negativism all over the country can breathe easier now that he has been removed from the forefront of the press *vs.* government battle. And perhaps they can even afford the luxury of feeling sorry for the man.

But his attack on the media was—and is, since he was obviously not speaking entirely for himself—a real threat to the free flow of information within America. Reporters have been jailed for reporting the news and refusing to divulge their confidential sources. Some, such as Jack Anderson's associate, Leslie Whitten, Jr., have even been not-so-neatly framed for alleged misconduct. Agnew's trying to calm the waters after the Watergate broke, by his statements that media fears of threats to their freedom were "fictional" and that there was no "grand conspiracy" in the administration to "nail the press," didn't do much to make the reporters in jail feel better.

Senator Sam Ervin put his finger on the real issue when he declared, "A press which is not free to gather news without threat of ultimate incarceration cannot play its role meaningfully. The people as a whole must suffer. For to make thoughtful and efficacious decisions—whether it be at the local school board meeting or in the voting booth—the people need information. If the sources of that information are limited to official spokesmen, the people have no means of evaluating the worth of their promise and assurances."

Harassment of journalists is currently the law of the land. In March 1972 the battle between the government and the press was in full swing. It had yielded few victories for the newsmen. Yet in a case growing out of the civil litigation between the Democratic National Committee and the Committee for the Re-Election of the President, reporters successfully resisted pressures to release confidential files, notebooks, and tapes. In the end, Judge Charles

Richey questioned the subpoenas the Committee to Re-Elect the President had obtained against ten reporters and executives of the New York *Times,* the Washington *Post,* the Washington *Star-News,* and *Time* magazine, on the grounds that they violated the newsmen's rights under the First Amendment.

"This court cannot blind itself," the judge said, "to the possible chilling effect the enforcement of these subpoenas would have on the press and the public."

The euphoria of journalists as a result of this landmark decision was short-lived. Three months later, the Supreme Court, by a 5—4 decision, declared, "We see no reason to hold that these reporters, any more than other citizens, should be excused from furnishing information that may help [a] grand jury . . ."

The decision specifically related to the case of New York *Times* reporter Earl Caldwell, whose work among West Coast Black Panthers brought him to the attention of a federal grand jury, which subpoenaed him to testify "concerning the aims, purposes, and activities of that organization." Caldwell argued that even a secret hearing would destroy the relationship he had struggled to gain in order to establish his sources. The High Court disagreed.

Since the Caldwell decision, judges, lawyers, and grand juries began subpoenaing newsmen with alarming frequency. As of April 1973, according to the Reporters' Committee for Freedom of the Press, more than thirty-five newsmen had been slapped with contempt citations for refusing to disclose confidential sources or material. Some have been jailed.

The whole issue was part and parcel of Nixon's "uncomfortable" feelings about the press, including his threats to *enforce* "fairness" in TV news reporting through the Federal Communications Commission's power to grant or withhold licenses and use antitrust legislation against the networks.

The chief concern, however, remains the question of a newsman's right to keep his sources confidential. A variety of solutions have been suggested. The Twentieth Century Fund is lobbying for a press council to monitor the performance of national news organizations. An American Bar Association study group recommended that the Association, generally a conservative group, support a nearly absolute closure of newsmen's confidential sources. They tend to agree with Peter Bridges, a reporter for the now-defunct Newark *News*, who declared, "A newsman must be granted immunity from being forced to divulge *any* information or source of identity before *any* investigating body."

The result of all this noise is a spate of state and federal legislation to try to solve the dilemma. Eighteen states have already put press-shield laws on their books. One of these eighteen states is New York. In New York, the law protects reporters from having to testify or having notes or tapes subpoenaed because of any information obtained while pursuing news. Which seems a very good solution to he "press shield" controversy.

Not everyone agrees, of course. Connecticut's Governor Thomas J. Meskill opposes shield legislation, finding little merit in "grubby little press cards." And State Senator Richard Berry of Maine says that a press bill should "give immunity to professional newsmen but not everyone whose pen is available for a dime." His definition of a professional was one who is "reasonable, intelligent, responsible and honest."

On the other extreme from Senator Berry is Governor Patrick J. Luccy of Wisconsin, who says that the law should protect the "lonely pamphleteer" as well as representatives of the established media—the Patrick Henrys as well as the Howard K. Smiths perhaps.

On the national level, over 50 bills designed to protect newsmen and their informants have been submitted in Congress (forty three in the House, thirteen in the Senate). Wisconsin Representative Robert Kastenmeier expects the number to exceed 100. Yet congressmen have run up against the same questions as their counterparts in the state legislature. How far should a shield law go?

The most likely alternative to cries for absolute privilege is the sort of "qualified" shield law providing protection only within a carefully defined limit. It's certainly the only kind of bill that would go through Congress. Senator Ervin's bill, which provides immunity unless a newsman had "actual personal knowledge which tends to prove or disprove the commission of the crime charged or being investigated," is a good sample of the "let's strike a balance" attitude that seems to be the order of the day.

But any time a new "definition" is made of an already existing protection—in this case, the Second Amendment, the right to redress of grievances—it seems the freedom becomes by definition more restricted. What's wrong with "Congress shall make no law . . . ?"

Chapter Eleven:

Future Trends

"I teach a course called the Psychology of Influence, and I begin it by stating categorically that the time has come when, if you give me any normal human being and a couple of weeks—maybe a couple of months—but I don't think so—I can change his behavior from what it is now to whatever you want it to be, if it's physically possible I can't make him fly by flapping his wings, but I can turn him from a Christian into a Communist and vice versa."—James McConnell, in Esquire *magazine*

"One pill makes you smaller, one pill makes you tall, and the ones that Mother gives you don't do anything at all. Go ask Alice when she's ten feet tall," go the words from a popular song of the psychedelic sixties written and cantillated by Grace Slick of the Jefferson Airplane. The words obviously referred to the then-flourishing youth-drug culture where consciousness-expanding pills made you taller and smaller according to a whim LSD and other scientific discoveries took the mind into realms unknown and unimagined by the previous generation, whose principal mode of transportation into the ethereal regions of highness had been alcohol, a drug which deadened rather than enhanced the senses.

Of course, there were found to be dangers in the pills; the "trips" were not all pleasure cruises. Some minds were found to lack the resilience to expand and then snap back to "normal." And

247

after a few trips with the drugs, the expansions became the normal forever. The kids—most of them—soon abandoned the pills in favor of other highs: religion, conformity, rural escape, and alcohol, to name a few.

And so the threat of the pills began to disappear. Or did it? Were LSD and related drugs only a tame prelude to what was really looming over the not-too-distant horizon, and would the day come when the taller and smaller pills would be put in the shadow by the pills for any image?

That day is almost here. A brain researcher from the University of California at San Diego predicted in January 1974 that scientists are on the verge of developing exquisite new drugs, without side effects, which will allow users to select the life style they desire for the moment.

The researchers refer to the drugs as chemical coping agents, which supposedly enable the takers to cope with their environment in the most efficient manner possible.

To give an example, suppose you are an executive in a large company. You seem to be stuck in a slot, and you are tired and overworked. A new project is about to begin and a new department head will be created. You want the job. In order to be considered, you need to come up with a brilliant idea that those in charge can not ignore. But you are tired and overworked and your brilliant idea won't form. What do you do? You take Pill A, of course, and for the next three months you will be active, creative, and dynamic.

For soldiers hockey players, and other individuals who need to be "up," Pill B will enable the individual to be a demon on wheels for a short time, mowing down the opposition in a surge of aggression undreamed-of by lesser men. Pussycat turns wildcat.

Dr. Arnold Mandell, chairman of the Department of Psychiatry at the University of California at San Diego, says that the chemical coping agents are a natural by-product of current brain research and, although potentially a beneficial medical breakthrough, just might have a few "worrisome" qualities, such as being able to alter states of mind in healthy persons.

These drugs are not yet available to the general public, but they do exist—some of them, anyway. One has the capacity to stimulate creativity and one has the specific property of making it more bearable to separate from a loved one.

Mandell believes that society will soon be forced to decide whether it is morally right to allow "normal" individuals to change themselves by taking a pill. Or, to re-write the lines of Grace Slick's song, "The ones that Mother gives you *will* do anything at all." What will happen to the world when Mother and Big Brother have the resources to change your behavior by slipping a white pill into your consommé?

That decision is not so far away. It is in the immediate future. It is currently called behavior-modification or aversion therapy, and it is no Clockwork Orange nightmare confined to fiction. It is an increasingly controversial technique used in the treatment of prison inmates, alcoholics, and juvenile offenders. Until February 14, 1974, the Law Enforcement Assistance Administration (LEAA) had funded many of the programs, but LEAA ordered an abrupt halt to such assistance at that time. However, the ban covered only that agency's funding and not money for such projects by the Bureau of Prisons or the Department of Health, Education, and Welfare. Also, there seems to be some question of just how the ban would be enforced.

The LEAA conceded that it did not know how many behavior-modification projects it is financing.

Aversion therapy has many facets. Besides the drugs mentioned earlier, it can be practiced by hypnosis, use of electronic hardware, and ordinary verbal suggestion. The patients range from volunteers who wish to cure a bad habit (such as nail-biting or excessive drinking) to mental patients who are sometimes placed in such programs without their consent.

Perhaps the worst abuses of behavior-modification take place in the nation's prisons. Inmates are given nausea-inducing drugs as a means of punishing antisocial behavior in some prisons, while in others electric shocks serve to discourage improper thoughts.

Research compiled by the American Civil Liberties Union's National Prison Project led to the termination of the START (an acronym for special treatment and rehabilitation training) program in a federal prison in Springfield, Missouri, where some inmates had been locked in tiny bare cells until they demonstrated correct behavior. Privileges would be gradually restored on a reward-and-punishment basis. START's finish may be only a first step, though, since there are at least fifteen more such programs around the country.

New ideas on behavior-modification are coming to light every day. One such idea has come from the UCLA center for the Study of Violence. The idea was for the implantation of electrodes in the brains of parolees which would then be "hooked" into a computer. The computer would monitor the brain patterns and administer shocks when it "read" violent behavior impulses. (It didn't seem to work on *The Terminal Man*.)

Some lawmakers suggest federal legislation to correct behavior-modification programs and aversion therapy techniques. Presently there are no laws on the subject, only some vague Federal Drug Administration regulations which govern the use of drugs. There are some legislative controls being contemplated, though, and among those are New York Democrat Charles Rangel's, which he plans to introduce in 1974 to the House.

Senator Sam Ervin has also been sounding the alarm about the behavior-modification programs. Among the issues, he said, were the rights to privacy, to dignity, to due process, and to equal protection of the laws. Senator Ervin was commenting specifically on the prison programs, and he suggested that a "moratorium" on funding of behavioral research be effected until adequate guidelines were legislated.

The American Psychological Association, the country's main organization of psychologists, said in a February 1974 statement that the banning of all such research and applied techniques "will result in a regression to outmoded, unsystematic forms of inhumanity in prisons that have characterized society's past treatment of its criminal offenders.

"Behavior modification involves a large number of procedures some of which are clearly abhorrent to psychologists as well as the public. Other procedures, however, are humane, benign, systematic, educational and effective."

Following is one example of behavior-modification which was "clearly abhorrent" and was practiced in the Iowa prison system until a United States Court of Appeals ruled in late 1973 that the program was cruel and unusual punishment.

The Iowa program used a drug called Apmorphine which was injected into prisoners without their consent. "When it was determined to administer the drug," the court wrote in its opinion, "the inmate was taken to a room near the nurses' station which contained only a water closet and there given the injection. He was then exercised and within about fifteen minutes he began vomiting. The vomiting lasted from fifteen minutes to an hour. There is also a temporary cardiovascular effect which involves some change in blood pressure and 'in the heart.' This aversion type 'therapy' is based on 'Pavlovian conditioning.' "

Another case took place a few years ago at two California institutions: Atascadero State Hospital for the Criminally Insane and the California Medical Facility at Vacaville, a psychiatric prison. It was determined to give more than one hundred "difficult" inmates the drug Anectine, which produces complete muscular paralysis and a halt to breathing for up to two minutes.

Individuals who have experienced it describe the result as similar to the feeling of drowning. As the drug was having its effect, the therapist would tell the patients that their "unacceptable behavior" was the cause of the terrifying situation they were in; they were warned that additional treatment would be needed if they didn't start to behave "acceptably."

Word of the program leaked out, and public criticism forced the researchers to drop the program. Luckily it leaked out. What if it hadn't? And in how many places has it not?

"The dividing line between aversion therapy and old-fashioned torture can become very thin and disappear altogether," says Edward M. Opton Jr., a senior psychologist at the Wright Institute, a graduate school of psychology in Berkeley, California.

Another California psychiatrist said, "It is immoral. It smacks of Big Brother and thought control, of humans turned into automatons."

But thought-control is only one of the future trends on which we must make decisions now—before it is too late. We must take firm control of these embryo menaces before they spring full-grown upon us and consume our individual freedom completely.

In the Introduction you met the Green family: Harold, his wife Helen, and their children, Dana, Michael, and David. Let's take that same family and project them into the future. Except for that projection the family remains essentially the same. Harold is forty-five, a sports buff, a taxpayer, and a home-owner. Helen runs her ceramics shop and Dana is a salesperson in a large department store. Michael is two years into a three-year government-service hitch, and David is a college student.

The most striking change in their lives is a great lessening of movement. Most of their lives are centered around and in the home. No longer does any member of the family have to travel to various places to pick over a bewildering array of brands and types of merchandise, and compare prices. There is only one brand of each type of item and only one price: government-controlled, government-tested, and government-approved. The reason for this is that all shopping is now done in the home via federally controlled cable television.

If Harold wants a new set of golf clubs, he presses out the code numbers for sports equipment generally and for golf clubs specifically on the little electronic box attached to his television set. Instantaneously a beautiful set of clubs appears on the tube, complete with analysis of wearability and price. Starting with the lowest priced, the pictures go on until the top line is reached. Harold can freeze the picture any time he wishes and return to any frame he chooses simply by pressing a freeze-and-replay button on top of the set.

(In 1973, in Orlando, Florida, five hundred homes were hooked up with two-way computer-controlled cable, which enables the viewer to send back digital responses to certain programs on the set. The Orlando experiment involves shopping by television—the viewer places his order by pushing the indicated buttons on the box attached to his set. A burglar-alarm system—which allows the police department to "monitor" the subscriber's apartment or home—opinion surveys, and pay television are also included in the experiment.)

Harold chooses a set which he feels will fit into his budget. The whole set will cost him one thousand credits. He decides to buy it. Harold pulls out his plastic identification card, which carries his chromosome passport, his thumbprint, his name, and—of course—his Social Security number. Inserting the card into the appropriate slot of the electronic box, Harold presses his thumb over the scanning window. If both prints match and his Social Security number is clear, the transaction will proceed, flashing over the airwaves to the linkup with the computer financial center. In a matter of seconds, his purchase is approved, the amount of one thousand credits is subtracted from his credit balance, and he is informed of delivery time. By three that afternoon, his new clubs will be delivered to his door. The card pops from the slot; Harold returns it to his pocket and goes back to work.

Harold's permanent identification card serves not only as money and as his international passport, but the key to his front door, his club locker, and his car as well. A tiny electronic computer attached to all locks scans the card inserted in the proper slot, compares the thumbprint, and either admits or refuses admission according to its evaluation of the comparison. A printout of the traffic going and coming is automatically recorded and available to anyone with access to the electronic lock keeper. There is no longer a need for private detectives. Lying about one's where-abouts at any time is, of course, futile. The cards can be canceled when lost, when rescinded, or when the bearer dies, by simply reprogramming the computer. All computers are owned by the government and reprogrammed by government agents only.

(As of January 1974, Washington, D.C., and twenty-nine states now provide photographs on drivers' licenses, and about half of them keep a negative of each photo on file. This can create a statewide file of mug shots on virtually every citizen. Polaroid equipment makes no negative; darkroom-developed cameras do, and so state legislatures and motor vehicle commissioners are faced with a decision of whether or not to opt for a negative file. The debate is upcoming in Illinois, New York, Kentucky, Penn-sylvania, South Dakota, Wisconsin, Maryland, Connecticut, Ar-kansas, Alabama, Nebraska, Mississippi, and Kansas in the months and years ahead.)

If that were to be combined with the following in some way, the United States would be on its way to having a federal identification card. Few Americans realize that there *is* a United States citizen identification card. One type is for citizens who regularly cross the Canadian border, another type is for presentation to immigration officers elsewhere in the country. The Department of Justice has announced that the two formats will be merged (38 Federal Regu-lation 8924, March 7, 1974) and that, according to regulation, "the U.S. citizen identification card will continue to be made available solely for the convenience of those U.S. citizens who wish to apply for it. Possession of the card is not mandatory." Photo identification cards, for welfare recipients are mandatory *now*, however, in most jurisdictions and failure to report for picturetaking is grounds for canceling welfare benefits.

If that weren't enough, the trend toward the use of the Social Security number as a universal identifier for all citizens continues unabated. A new bank that plans to serve military personnel —Services National Bank, Arlington, Virginia—will use the SSN as a checking account number. The American Bankers Association discourages the practice, but the bank points out that the SSN is already used to identify interest and dividend income for the IRS anyway. Further, the SSN now serves as armed forces service number.

Most colleges have abandoned student numbers and now use the SSN. New York Telephone and other phone companies around the nation request the SSN for identificaton and verification of new customers. Customers, however, should know that the telephone company "won't press the issue" if alternate identification or a personal appearance is offered.

Some Holiday Inns ask for the Social Security number. Travelers Insurance Company, one of the nation's largest, uses the SSN in place of separate policy numbers. L. Wheaton Smith of Palo Alto, California, refused his SSN, and Travelers issued him an independent policy number.

A Universal [sic] Identifier, used in Europe, allows the merging of information about individuals for administrative purposes. The HEW report on data banks in the summer of 1973 stated, "A permanent standard universal identifier issued at birth could create an incentive for institutions to pool or link their records, thereby making it possible to bring a lifetime of information to bear on any decision about a given individual."

The government and private computer car-pool selection systems insist on using an individual's Social Security number, although an entirely separate number would serve just as well, without increasing the use of the Social Security number as a universal identifier. Security of car-pool data-banks should be a major concern; the computers contain each individual's address and telephone and the hours he is away from home—also, in some cases, his hobbies and interests.

The government's standby rationing system, which was brought forth stillborn during the 1973-74 energy crunch, might still have to be brought to life someday. If so, it would require gas customers to sign name and license numbers at service stations, allegedly to prevent reuse of coupons. "Authorizations cards" prepared from state motor vehicle computer printouts will be mailed directly to each licensed driver. Conceivably, individual gas use would be monitored, or compared with existing data on car size and weight or distance from home to office, or used to trace an individual's travels around the country. All of this exists or could exist today.) Now let's return to the "futuristic" Green family.

The factory where Harold works is located over thirty miles from his home, but Harold's office is located in his den. Through a special cable television hookup, Harold is able to participate in executive meetings, dictate to his secretary, send or receive documents via a telefacsimile machine attached to the set, and supervise the operation of the factory. Most of the manual work of the factory is also done by other workers in the "privacy" of their homes via other cable TV hookups and remote control buttons. Each transaction of any importance can be recorded on videotape by any participant in the cable television hookup. It can also be recorded by inspectors if they so desire, for the National Business Bureau—an arm of the IRS—has access to all business transactions.

The same cable television with which Harold ordered his golf clubs serves not only as a shopping center for the entire family, but also as a combination newspaper, library, and theater.

(Besides the Orlando experiment described earlier, in an area of San Francisco where the cable company Viacom is franchised, four channels have been given over to educational uses for the 35,000 subscribers. A Viacom executive said the local archdiocese, working with other civic groups, accepted the responsibility for the programming.

In New York, a closed channel has been leased by Reuters for the instantaneous distribution of business information to its clients, and two Manhattan systems began in the early part of 1974 to use a data-transmission service for banks.)

A special attachment which is easily plugged into the main set enables the family to make "office visits" to the nearest health clinic without leaving their home. The clinics are all attached to the

Main National Health Center Data Bank, where all health records are kept. Also stored in the Center are the birth and death records and the latest medical knowledge. All of this information is readily available to the clinics and, of course, the government health inspectors and behavioral control specialists.

If it becomes necessary for any member of the family to have a personal doctor-patient encounter, the family car will take them to one of the clinics where a doctor is always on call. A permit to use the family car is, usually, easily obtained for such health purposes. Besides, the Greens have a good driving record and the electronic sensors have never yet reported them "lost."

(The *Cable Report* reported in 1973 that the Chicago Expressways include electronic sensors buried in the highway at half-mile intervals. They are there to measure traffic flow, but if every automobile had a tiny transmitter, Chicago's traffic computer could identify every car—say by license number—as it sped (perhaps beyond the speed limit) down the Dan Ryan Expressway. What's more, when Chicago finally gets a cable, the traffic system could be expanded anywhere the cable goes.)

The livingroom television center in the Greens' home serves also as the voting booth, two-way communication outlet, and educational classroom—although plug-in extensions for this purpose are available. Last night the Greens, along with four million other interested Americans, attended the opening of the National Opera. By inserting the family credit card into the slot on the set, the opening of the opera was televised into the Greens' living room. Their participation was recorded on videotape by the Government Cultural Commission for the purposes of planning future cultural events, and for "publication" in the television newspaper. The arts are flourishing and, if you happen to agree with the government's point of view, you will certainly be culturally satisfied.

(The federal government spent $375 million in fiscal year 1972 on audiovisual materials, including television and radio spots and motion pictures. The two agencies most involved were the

Pentagon and the United States Information Agency, according to an interagency study panel's report released in 1974 by the White House Office of Telecommunications Policy.

Clay Whitehead, director of the office, commented that the report was the first of its kind and revealed the surprising dimensions of government involvement with modern communications techniques. He called for immediate attention to the "potential for abuse, for turning public service messages into bureaucratic propaganda." He was not saying that there were such abuses; he was merely pointing out the areas in the government where there had been rapid growth and "no guidelines for the kinds of messages the Government ought to be sending out electrically or on film. Federal agencies are learning the value of sophisticated audiovisual techniques for getting their messages across, but no one has faced up to problems inherent in government wide use of such media techniques," he said. "We have to establish what messages provide valid and necessary information for the public. Above all, we don't want government telling us what to think.")

David Green, in his junior year of college, is studying Medical-Electronics and is presently attending a lecture on the advisability of implanting electrodes in all newborn babies, not only for the purposes of future identification, but for the direct computer-to-individual monitoring of brainwaves for purposes of adjudging the "normality" of all the citizens' brain patterns at all times. In this way—the professor lectures via the cable hookup —the person can be treated instantly for any tumors or other brain deformities, even before the patient himself is aware that anything is wrong.

He didn't mention—David notes on his special classroom video-recorder—that the electrodes might also be used for sociological and psychological purposes. For example, the electrodes might also be attached to the antidream machine, David muses, as his antidream-machine alarm goes off.

While David once again concentrates on his lecture, let us leave the Green family to fend for themselves in the future, and worry for the rest of the chapter about our fending with both the present and the future. For the electrodes and the dream machine already exist.

Although the electrode—called a brain pacemaker in medical circles—has been developed as a medical tool to help epileptic patients and other individuals with electrical brain disorders, it has caused some civil libertarians to wonder if it might not be used to enslave a population or turn soldiers into aggressive maniacs.

Dr. Jose M. R. Delgado, now at the University of Madrid Medical School and the National Social Security Center in Spain, does not believe that this will happen. He presented evidence at a 1974 symposium (on the relationship between mental disorders in man and animals) in New York City that shows that induced aggression must be latent in the individual to come out. "Thus, if a dominant monkey is so stimulated, it attacks its more submissive companion, but if a less dominant animal receives the stimulus, it makes only aggressive gestures. This, in turn, may provoke aggression by its dominant companion." The stimuli, Dr. Delgado said, "only evoke what is already there."

Another finding, he added, is that parts of the brain are tireless. One animal—a primate—was stimulated to grin 500,000 successive times. Its facial muscles grew tired, but the brain continued to respond as readily as ever.

If Dr. Delgado meant those comments to allay the fears of the robot population, his well-intentioned meanings were far short of his goal.

The dream machine was designed by scientist Karel Monto in the early seventies and was initially tested at the United States Naval Academy. When the volunteer midshipmen began to daydream at their desks, about their girlfriends or some lazy South Sea isle, Bong! they were found out. It was discovered that the machine really helped the mind to concentrate.

There are other ways of helping the mind to concentrate, as Samuel Johnson pointed out quite some time ago when he remarked that the prospect of hanging wonderfully concentrates the mind. But it is doubtful if we wish to concentrate the mind in that manner. The prospect of hanging is a rather tangible example of a definite end; the dream machine is not so tangible nor so definite, but it seems to us it would bring the end of something we are better off not losing.

Listed below are a few other trends which might bear watching, lest they become future subjects of abuse.

Trial by television: In 1973, in Vermont, the first video tape trial took place. The reason the experiment was attempted was explained by R. Grant Brady, an audiovisual specialist for the National Center of State Courts in Denver: "When a judge tells a jury, 'disregard that statement,' everyone knows that they don't disregard that statement." So Mr. Brady directed the use of videotape equipment when a jury convicted a man in a trial in which testimony was prerecorded and shown on closed-circuit television. To avoid monotony, Mr. Brady and an assistant used two cameras to tape the testmony from various angles, occasionally zooming in for a close-up of a witness or a document admitted into evidence. The tape was then edited in the presence of and with the assent of the prosecutor, the defense, and the judge. As was previously stated, the jury convicted the defendant.

Since then other versions of trial by television, or Trialevision, have been used in several other states, including Colorado, Illinois, Iowa, and Wisconsin. In Sandusky, Ohio, fourteen civil rights cases were taped and the testimony of the witnesses were shown on TV monitors to the jury. The juries rendered verdicts without ever seeing a single witness in the flesh.

The argument for the trialevision experiments is that it saves considerable time. The fourteen trials in Sandusky were completed in eleven working days. Normally the trial judge, McCrystal, estimated that the same cases tried in the conventional "live" way would have taken forty to forty-five days. And with the country's court dockets so packed, that is a plus to be considered.

It is admitted that criminal trials will probably never be completely videotaped, since the complicated and tangled web of a citizen's rights would probably be violated by such a process, but that civil cases would more than likely be videotaped in the near future.

The danger we see here is the same one that lurks behind every aspect of human endeavor and that is a great potential for abuse. A government-controlled trial could easily be staged behind the scenes with the defendant unable to reach any juror's ear with his own live voice. The edited tapes could be made to say almost anything, and the jury would never be the wiser. It is another step toward complete control of citizens' lives, if it is so used. And who is to guarantee it wouldn't be?

The sale of information: The United States Department of Commerce, which sells magnetic tapes of taxpayer data by zip codes as well as nonpersonal governmental reports and statistics, now lets business executives charge such purchases by American Express cards.

The computer systems: CLEAR (County Law Enforcement Applied Regionally) is Cincinnati's name for its computerized file on criminals. In Pennsylvania, it's CLEAN (Commonwealth Law Enforcement Assistance Network). In Illinois, it LEADS (Law Enforcement Agencies Data System), but in Massachusetts it LEAPS (Law Enforcement Agencies Processing System.)

The Kansas City police call their system ALERT II (Automatic Law Enforcement Response Time); Connecticut has CONNECT (Connecticut On-Line Enforcement Communications and Tele-processing); Lowell, Massachusetts has a BEAT (Breaking, Entering, and Auto Theft) program; Los Angeles has ORACLE (Optimum Record Automation for Courts and Law Enforcement); and in Missouri, of course, it's MULES (Missouri Uniform Law Enforcement System). The University of Oklahoma retrieves legal information via GIPSY (General Information Processing System).

There are many, many others. All performing well-intentioned law-enforcement, legal duties for the citizens. The only thing we worry about is if MULES get BEAT and GIPSY LEAPS to the

ALERT and CONNECTS with CLEAN ORACLE. Then we've had it.

Supreme Court decisions: Lost in the Watergate Wallowing was a Supreme Court action which could well mean gag-ruling on the press. The High Court did not rule on the case in point; rather, it voted not to hear the case. (Justice William O. Douglas was the only dissenting member of the Court).

What they refused to hear was this: Two Louisiana reporters —Larry Dickinson of the Baton Rouge *Sun-Times* and Gibb Adams of the Baton Rouge *Morning Advocate*—were covering a case in the United States District Court in New Orleans. The case involved a suit filed by a man who alleged that the state had brought a murder case against him not to convict, but rather to harass. In the course of the trial, the district judge, E. Gordon West, ruled that "no report of the testimony taken in this case today shall be made in any newspaper or by radio or television, or by any other media." He was doing this, he said, "in order to avoid undue publicity which could in any way interfere with the rights of the litigants in connection with any further proceedings."

Reporters Dickinson and Adams knew the order to be unconstitutional and ignored it. Their respective newspapers ran their bylines on the court stories. They were both subsequently convicted of criminal contempt and fined three hundred dollars each. Appealing the case to the United States Court of Appeals for the Fifth District, the two reporters were told that Judge West's order had been in violation of the First Amendment, but that they were still liable for the fines. "There remains the very formidable question of whether a person may, with impunity, knowingly violate an order which turns out to be invalid. We hold that in the circumstances of this case he may not."

Judge West again convicted the reporters and fined them the three hundred dollars each. Again the higher court ruled, although the original order was unconstitutional, they had to pay the fines.

They then asked the High Court to hear the case. When the Supreme Court would not, the decision stood.

"A most alarming opinion," said the Society of Newspaper Editors. "One can be assured that this will give great impetus to judges entering gag orders around the country. . . . We must ask if this means that the courts have now become self-imposed censors of the press in this country?"

In another "alarming opinion" by the Supreme Court, the power of law-enforcement officers to search persons without a warrant was upheld. On a vote of 6 to 3, the Court said that a person taken into custody on minor charges (such as going through a red light) may then be searched for evidence of more serious but unrelated crimes. As long as the officer has made a valid custodial arrest—one that can take the person to the station—the officer can search the person thoroughly, and "no additional justification" is needed.

One of the dissenting justices, Thurgood Marshall, said that the ruling raised "the possibility that a police officer, lacking probable cause to obtain a search warrant, will use a traffic arrest as a pretext to conduct a search."

But things are not all bad. Every cloud has a silver lining no matter how tattered. In Dale Menard's case, the tattered lining was five years old. That was the length of time he had fought with the FBI, through the courts to have his fingerprints removed from their criminal activity file

If you have forgotten the Menard case, here is a short recap: When he was nineteen, Menard was arrested in a Los Angeles park. Two policemen saw another man's wallet on the ground near him. He was booked for burglary, fingerprinted, and held for more than two days. No complaint was filed and no evidence was found to prove that he had stolen the wallet in question or even if the wallet had indeed been stolen in the first place. But his fingerprints routinely went to the FBI. In his file was this notation under

"Disposition of case"—"Released—unable to connect with any felony or misdemeanor at this time."

He won his case in 1974—in a way. The court ruled that the FBI could keep his prints, but in a neutral non-criminal file, and that there could be no reference to indicate "that the prints originated in a source for criminal files."

But the important thing in the Menard case is that he fought. He at least had the courage of his convictions to pursue the fight for his rights to the end. If he had had the support of the media and the people, his fight would not have taken so long. If we care—as Dale Menard did—about our right to privacy, we had better begin our fight now. Write to your congressman, support legislation designed to protect you. Remember your privacy is a precious commodity, and once given up, it is very difficult to recover.

If that isn't enough to cheer you on, listen to these words by a famous statesman: "Many things are necessary to lead a full, free life, such as good health and a fair break in the market place.

"But none of these is more important than the most basic of all individual rights, the right to privacy. A system that fails to respect its citizen's right to privacy fails to respect the citizens themselves."—Richard M. Nixon, February 23, 1974.

Bibliography

BOOKS

Asch, Sidney H., *Police Authority and the Rights of the Individual* (Arco Publishing Co., New York, 1971)

Becker, Theodore L. and Murray, Vernon G., *Government Lawlessness In America*, (Oxford University Press, New York, 1971)

Block, Eugene, *Fingerprinting*, (David McKay Co., Inc., New York, 1969)

Brenton, Myron, *The Privacy Invaders*, (Coward McCann, Inc. New York 1964)

Campbell, James S. et al, *Law and Order Reconsidered, Task Force Report to the National Commission on the Causes and Prevention of Violence*, (Bantam Books, New York, 1970)

Chevigny, Paul, *Police Power*, (Pantheon Books, New York, 1969)

Crombach, Lee J., *Essentials of Psychological Testing*, (Harper & Row, New York, 1960)

DelGado, Jose M. R., MC., *Physical Control of the Mind (To ward a Psychological Society,)* (Harper & Row, New York, 1969)

Freeman, Frank S., *Theory and Practice of Psychological Testing*, (Holt, Reinhart and Winston, New York, 1966)

Garrison, Omar V., *Spy Government: The Emerging Police State in America*. (Lyle Stuart, New York, 1969)

Golomb, Solomon W., et al., *Digital Communications with Space Applications*, (Prentice Hall, Englewood Cliffs, NJ, 1964)

Goulden, Joseph C., *Monopoly* (Simon & Schuster, Inc., New York, 1970)

265

Handel, S., *The Electronic Revolution* (Penguin Books, Middlesex, England, 1967)

Lieberman, Jethro K., *How the Government Breaks The Law*, (Penguin Books, Baltimore, 1973)

Miller, Arthur R., *The Assault on Privacy*, (New American Library, New York, 1971)

Nelson, Jack and Ostrow, Ronald J., *The FBI and the Berrigans*, (Coward, McCann and Geoghegan, Inc., New York, 1972)

Ollestad, Norman, *Inside the FBI*, (Lyle Stuart, New York, 1967)

Pennock, J. Roland and Chapman, John W. (ed.) *Privacy* (Atherton Press, New York, 1969)

Ransom, Harry Howe, *Central Intelligence and the National Security* (Harvard University Press, Cambridge, 1958)

Reiss, Albert J., Jr., *The Police and the Public*, (Yale University Press, New Haven, 1971)

Rosenberg, Jerry M., *The Death of Privacy*, (Random House, New York, 1969)

Skolnick, Jerome, *The Politics of Protest*, (Ballantine Books, New York, 1969)

Spindel, Bernard B., *The Ominous Ear*, (Award House, New York, 1968)

Tully, Andrew, *White Tie and Dagger* (William Morrow and Co., New York, 1967)

Turner, William W., *Invisible Witness*, (Bobbs-Merrill Co., Inc., New York, 1968)

———, *Uncle Sam is Watching You: Highlights from the Senate Subcommittee on Constitutional Rights*, (Public Affairs Press, Washington, D.C., 1971)

Watters, Pat and Gillers, Stephen (ed.), *Investigating the FBI* (Doubleday and Co., Garden City, N.Y., 1973)

Whitehead, Don, *The FBI Story*, (Random House, New York, 1956)

Wise, David and Ross, Tom B., *The Invisible Government*, (Random House, New York, 1964)

PERIODICALS

"Bugging The Bedroom," *Esquire*, Vol. 60, May, 1966, pp 97 +
"Card Carrying Readers," *New Republic*, Vol. 163, July 25, 1970, p.7
"Dirty Business," *Nation*, Vol. 203, Dec. 26, 1966, pp. 690-1
Mayer, Martin, "The Loneliness of the Short Distance Dialer," *Esquire*, Vol. 64, October, 1970.
". . . of 1984", *Nation*, Vol. 210, July 1, 1970, pp. 648-51.
Nader, Ralph, "Invasion of Privacy," *Saturday Review*, Vol. 54, April 17, 1971, pp. 18-21.
The Nation, Vol. 212, February 22, 1971, pp. 321-2.
"Privacy and the 1970 Census," *National Review*, Vol. 21, March 11, 1969, pp. 220-1
"Snooping on the Home Front," *The Nation*, Vol. 211, October 5, 1970, pp. 305-6.
"The Big Snoop," *Life*, Vol. 60, No. 20, May 20, 1966, pp. 38 +
"Thirty Years of Wiretapping," *The Nation*, Vol. 212, June 14, 1971, pp. 744-50.
U.S. News and World Report, Vol. 70, Feb. 22, 1971, pp. 38-41.
And *Time* Magazine, *The New York Times*, *The New York Post*, *The Privacy Report*

Index

269